THE LIBRARY OF NURSING

The Royal College of Nursing and
National Council of Nurses of the United Kingdom

Henrietta Place, Cavendish Square,
London, W.1

If sent through the Post this Book must be soundly protected.
It is due to be returned unless renewed, on:—

EXTRACT FROM RULES.

No book shall be kept longer than one month without its renewal having been applied for within that period. If the book is overdue **a fine of 1s. must be paid immediately, and an additional charge of 3d. a week will be made until the book is renewed or returned. The privilege of bor-** rowing further books is suspended, until the fine is paid. Any books lost or damaged must be replaced or the damage made good by the last borrower of the book, whether an individual reader or Group borrower. Any borrower who is in contact with any infectious or contagious diseases should notify the Librarian if any borrowed book which she possesses should have come into direct contact with any infected person. Such a book should be held until instructions have been received from the Librarian.

Your Body

Its Anatomy
and Nutrition

Your Body
Its Anatomy
and Nutrition

by

S. William Kalb, M.D.
F.A.C.B., F.A.C.N.

and

Christian A. Hovde, Ph.D.
Department of Anatomy
Seton Hall College of Medicine and Dentistry

C. S. Hammond & Company

MAPLEWOOD, N. J.

Distributed by:
OLDBOURNE PRESS
1-5 Portpool Lane, London, E.C.1.

© Copyright 1962 C. S. Hammond & Company
Maplewood, New Jersey

Library of Congress Catalog Card Number 62-11652
Printed in U.S.A.

Reproduction in whole or in part
prohibited without written permission
from the publisher.

Table of Contents

The male and female anatomy are represented in unique, full-color die cut illustrations. When the cutouts are detached along the perforations, the body layers and organs fall one upon the other in correct position and proportion for fullest understanding of their inter-relationships.

6

Introduction

For thousands of years the human body has been the greatest mystery recognized by man in his physical world. No matter how much has been discovered by physicians and research workers over the past centuries there has always remained an almost overwhelming mass of unsolved problems. Today, with the modern methods available, trained men and women have been able to solve some of these problems of the past, but in doing so they have uncovered many new problems to be solved in the future.

When men knew very little about the physical structure of the body, they began their work by studying how the body was put together—its anatomy. They dissected the muscles, bones, nerves and other tissues and worked out their relationship to one another. Once the bones had been named and the effect of individual muscles on particular bones and joints had been established, study progressed to the internal workings of these parts of the body. Each type of tissue was found to have certain specific functions and these functions were at least in part related to the anatomy of the individual tissue types. This led to the use of the microscope to see what sort of cell arrangement was present in the organs of the body. With this came the study of the chemical and physical characteristics of the secretions of the various organs and of the individual cells. Scientists are still striving to discover how the individual cells function and to describe them in finer detail.

In order to understand and care for the body properly, one

must begin with a study of its anatomy, its parts and the functions of those parts. This book is designed to aid in that study by introducing the subject to the reader. It cannot do much more than introduce the subject since a full discussion of the material presented here fills hundreds of thick volumes in medical libraries. Even doctors and scientists cannot possibly read all of these, but must concentrate on certain portions of the total picture.

However, it is important that everyone should know something about the way his or her body is put together for this makes it possible to evaluate intelligently the knowledge handed down from the past and to utilize the most modern recent information. With some idea of the anatomy of the body many baseless fears may be eliminated and replaced with facts tested and proved in the laboratories and hospitals. The most important thing that a book of this type can do is to provide the information which will enable the reader to recognize the normal conditions and actions of the body and to seek proper, well-trained advice when the normal becomes abnormal.

This book does not pretend to equip the reader to diagnose his own ills. It is hoped, though, that it will aid in his appreciation of the beauty and complexity of the human body; increase his knowledge of its functions; and emphasize that the best policy with regard to injuries or disorders of that body is an immediate physical examination by a doctor or dentist. It should also provide a stimulus for the establishment of a regular physical examination schedule as a means of preventing small problems from becoming large ones through neglect.

Chapter One

BONE AND BONE DEVELOPMENT

Bone, one of the hardest substances in the body, develops from a softer substance in most cases. This substance is called *cartilage*. A cartilage model of the long bones of the arms and legs develops in the embryo about the time muscle tissue begins to develop. Gradually, the model is broken down and replaced by inorganic salts of minerals such as calcium and potassium, deposited at first in the cartilage matrix and later in a true bone matrix. Contrary to popular belief, bone is very much alive. It has cells and blood vessels to deliver food and provide for exchange of gases such as oxygen and carbon dioxide. It is so variable, in fact, that its content is not the same from one day to the next. Minerals present in bone are constantly being removed and used elsewhere in the body, and new supplies are deposited in their place. Bone thus acts as a bank or reservoir for some of the materials needed by other parts of the body.

Bones also change their shape and size in response to stimuli impressed upon them from the outside. For example, a baby's bones are quite different from those of an adult. An adult is able to walk and support his weight on the bones of his legs and feet while a baby cannot do these things. The bones of an adult show the effect of weight and particularly the effect of muscles pulling on the bones at various points. Adult bones from the body of a bed-ridden person, who has not walked for perhaps a year, compared to those of a well person who has walked during this period, are smoother, lighter and less strong. After the sick person has recovered and begins to walk, his bones change to match the different stress situation. They become rough where the muscles pull against them. The walls of the shaft become thicker and heavier in response to the addition of weight and muscular exertion.

Bones are not solid throughout. Only when the cartilage model first appears is it solid throughout its length. As the model is changed gradually into bone, the center portion of the bone is hollowed out and no solid matter is deposited therein. This is called the *marrow cavity*. It is filled with blood vessels and connective tissue. In the marrow, blood cells are produced and then carried out into the blood stream. Doctors sometimes examine very small parts of this marrow material to see whether or not blood cell production is proceeding normally. Such an examination, made under a microscope, is called a *biopsy*.

Long bones are divided into several parts: the shaft or diaphysis, the neck, the marrow cavity, the epiphyseal plate and the
epiphysis. The *shaft* is the long thick-walled part of the bone between the two ends of the bone. Contained inside the shaft is the
marrow cavity. At the end of the marrow cavity is the *neck* of the
bone. Beyond the neck is a region known as the *epiphyseal plate.*

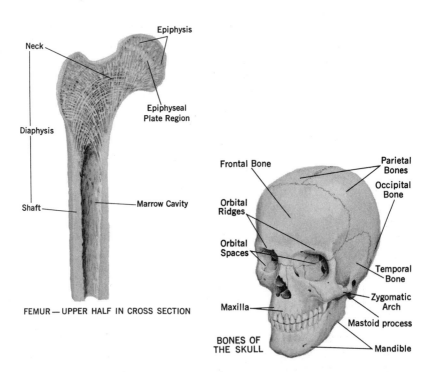

Epiphysis

Neck

Epiphyseal
Plate Region

Diaphysis

Shaft ———— Marrow Cavity

FEMUR — UPPER HALF IN CROSS SECTION

Frontal Bone

Parietal
Bones

Occipital
Bone

Orbital
Ridges

Orbital
Spaces

Temporal
Bone

Zygomatic
Arch

Maxilla

Mastoid process

BONES OF
THE SKULL

Mandible

In a young person, whose bones are still growing in length, the
epiphyseal plate is composed of cartilage. Bone of the diaphysis
lies on one side of the plate while the bone of the epiphysis lies
on the other side. As the cartilage grows in thickness, the bone's
length increases, and the shaft is made longer in order to cover the
thickening cartilage plate. The portion of the cartilage plate thus
covered by bone is then broken down and replaced by new bone,
or a space is created, lengthening the marrow cavity as well as
the shaft.

When the total normal length of the bone has been reached
in the growth process, the epiphyseal plate is broken down and replaced by bone. Once the plate has become bone, no further
growth in length is possible. Normally this only happens at the end

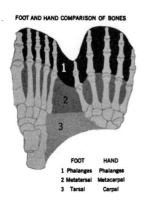

FOOT AND HAND COMPARISON OF BONES

FOOT	HAND
1 Phalanges	Phalanges
2 Metatarsal	Metacarpal
3 Tarsal	Carpal

of the full growth period, around the age of 18 or 20 years. Obviously, if fusion of the plate should occur at an earlier age, before the full length of the bones has been reached and the growth process is thereby stopped, that person's growth in overall body height would also be halted and he would remain permanently short. Premature fusion of the epiphyseal plate is, of course, not the only cause of short stature. Indeed, it is rather a rare occurrence. But it does contribute to an understanding of the manner in which the bone grows.

The marrow cavity, the space in the center of the shaft, has two functions: 1. to aid in the lightening and strengthening of the bone (a tube is stronger than a bar of the same material) and, 2. to provide a space in which the blood cells develop.

The blood cells develop from certain other cells called *stem cells*. There are two main types of blood cells, the red and the white. The red cells function as the medium whereby oxygen and carbon dioxide are carried to and from the tissues of the body, while the white cells serve as the soldiers defending the body against attack by bacilli and other disease agents. The white cells attempt to kill and isolate the disease agents by engulfing them. In the process, some of the white cells themselves die and form the material we know as *pus*.

Blood cell production depends on a good, adequate and well-balanced diet. If the proper food materials and minerals are not present, the body cannot function. Iron is necessary, for example, for the proper functioning of the red cells. It is used to form an essential chemical compound called *hemoglobin*. It is the hemoglobin which is used to carry oxygen through the blood stream. Without iron, hemoglobin cannot carry oxygen and the body starves when the oxygen is not present.

To do their part efficiently, bones must be properly formed; that is, they must contain a sufficient quantity of mineral salts derived from food intake. They must also be exercised at more or less regular intervals in order to maintain their useful structure.

In old age, the mineral constitution of the bone changes again. At this time, bones may become somewhat brittle and less able to resist shock. Also there is often a reduced capacity in the body's ability to repair a broken bone.

Chapter Two

MUSCLES

The muscles used to walk, run, lift heavy loads, support weight on the back, or turn the head are called *voluntary muscles* or *skeletal muscles*. Their prime function is the movement and support of the various portions of the skeleton. Since these muscles are composed of millions of individual muscle cells, each of which has a striated or cross-banded appearance under the microscope, they are referred to by biologists as *striated muscles*. Normally they will shorten or contract whenever we want them to. Another muscle type included in the family of striated muscle is *cardiac muscle*. This muscle is different, however, for we cannot stop or start contraction of it at will. It is, therefore, an *involuntary* striated muscle. Muscles found in the area of the stomach and the intestinal tract, and those controlling the blood vessels are also involuntary, but these are the *non-striated* or *smooth* type of muscle.

MICROSCOPIC APPEARANCE OF MUSCLE

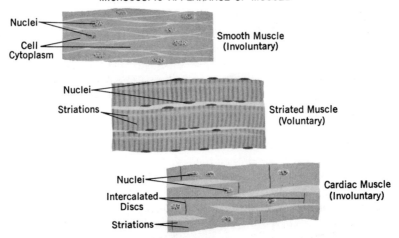

Nuclei

Cell
Cytoplasm

Smooth Muscle
(Involuntary)

Nuclei

Striations

Striated Muscle
(Voluntary)

Nuclei

Intercalated
Discs

Striations

Cardiac Muscle
(Involuntary)

It follows that each type of muscle performs a different job and is specialized in its construction. Skeletal muscle fibers are large in diameter, rather long, and are found in bundles in which all the cells run in the same direction. The arrangement of fibers with one another, and the bundles of fibers (muscles as we usually think of them), with the bones to which they are attached, provide very fast contraction and very powerful contraction for short periods of time. Thus large amounts of work can be performed with this type of muscle.

Smooth muscle fibers, on the other hand, are shorter in length and of smaller diameter. These fibers are arranged in sheets, rather than bundles, and several sheets may lie one on top of another. Within each sheet all the fibers run in the same direction, but the sheets are arranged so that the direction of fibers is different.

It is striated muscle that makes up a great portion of the thickness of the chest and abdominal wall; it is striated muscle that forms the solid-looking arms and legs in the non-fat person. But the muscular portion of the walls of the esophagus, the stomach, and the small and large intestine are composed of smooth muscle. This is also found in most of the soft portions of the body. Cardiac muscle is present in one place only—the muscular wall of the heart.

An intimate relationship exists between muscle and the nervous system. Voluntary and involuntary muscles both rely on the body's communication system and, in order to operate, the muscular parts of the body must be driven by it. The intimacy of the relationship between the striated type of muscle and the nervous system can be demonstrated. Should nerves to striated muscles of the arm or leg be cut, separating the muscles from the spinal cord, we know that the muscles would gradually waste away and become small and useless. This process, known as *atrophy,* takes time. However, if the nerve ends can be brought together again and kept there, the nerve may regenerate, sending new fibers to the muscle. If the fibers reach the muscle cells successfully and re-establish proper connections, the muscle may be saved and function established again. If, on the other hand, proper connections cannot be re-established, the muscle becomes permanently damaged and even ceases to function.

There are other ways in which muscle wastage occurs. The most important and usual of these is disuse or lack of activity. If muscle tissue is not used regularly and nearly at its fullest capacity for work, it becomes smaller and harder to use. Failure to exercise can cause a temporary loss of function. If the particular muscles in question are not used, it may be impossible to make them work at all after a long period. This type of disfunction is called "atrophy of disuse."

Everyone has seen the results of exercise in developing musculature as illustrated in certain advertisements in newspapers, magazines, or on T.V. While some of this is possible, it is not always true that every man, no matter what his age or physical condition, can attain the physical perfection he desires. What is true is that exercise is necessary and desirable in maintaining the physi-

14

cal condition essential for long life and full functional activity. The important point is that exercise should be taken regularly and with care as to the amount and the plan. Excessive general exercise practiced at wide intervals can be damaging rather than helpful while mild exercise, done regularly and continued over a long period of time, is good for the whole structure of the body. Patients with certain types of heart trouble are now being advised by their physicians to exercise mildly each day in order to improve the general condition of the body, making it easier for the heart to do its work.

Growing children will exercise normally and usually to the proper degree without thinking about it. When these same children grow up, acquire responsibility, and in large measure give up the spontaneous physical activity of childhood, they need a sensible and regular schedule of exercise. The schedule should be planned by a physician, especially if the program is begun late in life. To derive the maximum benefit, the program should be followed faithfully by the patient.

Chapter Three
NERVOUS SYSTEM

The complete nervous system consists of two major portions: A. The *peripheral nervous system* (or peripheral nerves) and B. The *central nervous* system which includes the spinal cord and the brain. The peripheral and the central nervous systems are joined together and are one complete functional system.

The peripheral nervous system (PNS) is the name given to the bundles of nerve fibers or *neurons* that begin at the spinal cord and reach out to the skin, to individual skeletal muscles, and to the internal organs such as the stomach and the intestinal tract. These "nerves" contain, in general, two types of neurons; that is, neurons serving two general functions, namely *motor* and *sensory.* The sensory neurons are responsible for transmitting information from the skin, the muscles and the internal organs to the central nervous system. The motor neurons are responsible for carrying information from the central nervous system (CNS) to the muscles in order that they may react properly to the situation. For example, when you touch a very hot iron with your finger, the sensory neuron endings in the skin touching the iron and just beneath it "feel" the hotness of the iron and discharge along the nerve into the spinal cord of the CNS. There these fibers contact other cells among which are some that are motor in function. These cells "fire" and their fibers or *axons* carry the information back to certain muscles of the hand and arm. The result is a rapid movement of these parts of the body away from the hot iron. This type of movement is often called *reflex movement* and the neurons involved are called the *reflex arc.* Reflex movement does not depend on our conscious feeling that the iron is hot. It can operate even when the spinal cord is separated from the brain completely.

The conscious sensation of pain and/ or temperature (warm or cold) is a function of the brain and specifically of a part of the cerebral cortex. The sensory neurons which bring the information to the spinal cord for the reflex action also transmit the same information to another group of cells in the spinal cord which send it upward toward the brain. These secondary neurons send the message first to a nucleus called the *thalamus,* a cen-

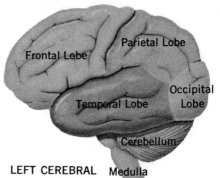

Frontal Lobe   Parietal Lobe   Occipital Lobe   Temporal Lobe   Cerebellum   Medulla

LEFT CEREBRAL CORTEX

tral brain receiving station, and from there it is transmitted to the portion of the cerebral cortex which is concerned with sensory information. Once this information reaches the cerebral sensory cortex we "feel" the hot iron, and can consciously act on the information (in contrast to the reflex action performed by the spinal cord). In the same way we can "feel" such sensations as pain,

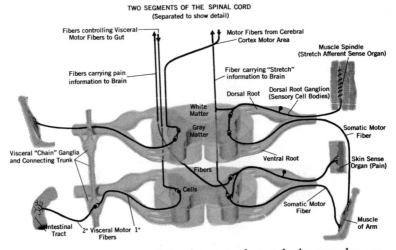

TWO SEGMENTS OF THE SPINAL CORD
(Separated to show detail)

temperature, pressure, and the amount of stretch the muscles are undergoing. The latter is interesting since this information provides an estimate of the position of the limbs and trunk when "stretch afferent" information from all the affected muscles is received in the cortex and correlated. Thus, when we put a hand behind our back we "know" where the hand is in relation to the rest of the arm and body, and can use this information to pick up an object which we cannot see, or to place the hand or the foot wherever we may wish. This is called *proprioception*.

If the sensory neurons carrying the primary information from the muscles to the spinal cord, or the secondary neurons relaying the information upward to higher centers are injured, we then cannot "find" and/or do not "know" where the hand is. We can still move the hand but now we must see where the hand is in order to move it to the proper place. In other words, we must substitute sight for the lost proprioceptive sense. Since we do not normally pay close attention to the exact position of our hands and feet, suddenly finding ourselves in the position of having to do so is awkward, and we do things slowly and with great attention to every detail of the motion, watching our feet and hands to see that they are placed in the proper location.

The *somatic system* produces precise information requiring precise and rapid action, while the *visceral system* produces general information requiring slower, more generalized activity. The nerves, which acquire information from the internal organs of the body and send these organs the motor stimuli which they need to act, are called *visceral* in order to distinguish them from the *somatic* fibers just described. In general, these nerve fibers do the same things for the internal organs as the somatic nerves do for the skeletal muscle system. Visceral motor nerves, however, are connected to the glands, the smooth muscle of the gut-walls, and the blood vessels, while the somatic motor nerve fibers are connected only to the skeletal muscles moving the head, trunk, and limbs. Ordinarily, the information derived from the visceral sensory nerve fibers does not reach our conscious thinking levels. We are not aware of the things happening inside of us unless something is wrong with the normal operation of one of the internal organs. Even when something is wrong and we "feel" it, we cannot localize the pain as easily as we can when similar painful information is sent by the somatic sensory system to the brain. Thus, there is an apparent difference in the purpose of their information.

The spinal cord, the first part of the central nervous system, receives the information transmitted to it by the sensory cells lying in the dorsal root ganglion, and sends motor impulses to the muscles of the body via the motor nerves, both visceral and somatic. The spinal cord also connects the body with the brain, as we have explained previously.

The brain is divided into several major sections: the cerebral hemispheres, including the cortex; the basal ganglia; the thalamus; the hypothalamus; the cerebellum; the medulla.

The *cerebral cortex* is the so-called "conscious" brain. The information that reaches the cortex is recognized by the person and conscious decisions based on that information can be made.

The cortex has been divided, somewhat arbitrarily, into four parts on each side of the brain; the frontal, parietal, occipital, and temporal lobes.

The "front end" of the *frontal lobe* is thought to be concerned with the emotions of the individual, although the information justifying this assignment is still rather scant. It is known that the posterior portion of the *frontal lobe* is concerned with willful motor movement. This is the area we use when we decide that we want to use the right hand to pick up an object, or to put the right foot on the stair. This type of movement must be distinguished from reflex movement shown by the spinal cord.

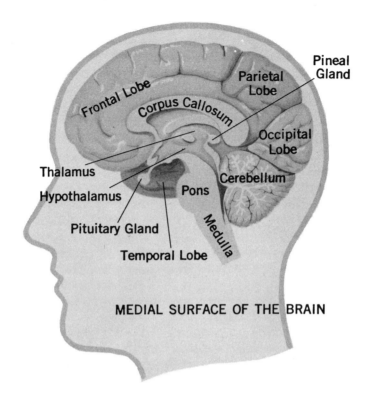

Pineal
Gland

Parietal
Lobe

Frontal Lobe

Corpus Callosum

Occipital
Lobe

Thalamus

Cerebellum

Hypothalamus

Pons

Pituitary Gland

Medulla

Temporal Lobe

MEDIAL SURFACE OF THE BRAIN

The *parietal lobe* is concerned with the receipt of sensory information from the body, exclusive of the "special senses" (sight, smell, taste, and hearing). The surface of the cortex can be divided into special areas in which sensation from the hand, the face and the foot can be distinguished separately.

The *occipital lobe* is primarily concerned with the sense of sight, while the *temporal lobe* is concerned with hearing and smell, among other things.

Damage to the posterior portion of the frontal lobe in the motor area results in paralysis. That is, it is no longer possible to move the arm, the hand, or the fingers on the opposite of the body. The limb will still react to stimuli by reflex action, but it is unable to react when "willed" to move. This type of paralysis may also be caused by damaging the fibers leading from the cells of the cortex downward to the spinal cord.

When the occipital cortex or temporal cortex is damaged, the sensation of sight or hearing is lost. The eyes and the ears still function perfectly, but the incoming information from them cannot be interpreted on a conscious level by the brain.

The *basal ganglia,* lying below the cortex and at the front end of the brain, are responsible for the associated movements of the body. They are responsible for seeing that all movements which go into an action take place. For example, when we throw a ball, the arm does the throwing, but the opposite leg, arm and the trunk also take part in the movement. If the basal ganglia are injured, the associated movements are poor or absent, and only the arm throwing the ball will be moved.

The *thalamus* receives a great deal of information (sensory) sent by the sensory nerve fibers through the spinal cord to the brain. In the thalamus, a certain amount of analysis takes place, and the information is routed to the proper end stations in subcortical and cortical areas.

The *hypothalamus,* an area lying at the base of the brain just below the thalamus, is responsible for the maintenance of body temperature, blood pressure, water regulation, and other basic functions necessary to life. Also, by its close anatomic connection with the pituitary gland, it has been implicated in the control of endocrine gland function.

The *cerebellum* lies behind the cerebral hemispheres and over the medulla. Its function has been accurately described as concerned with *synergy*—the quality of controlling muscles so that they work together smoothly, cleanly, and without faltering or mismovement. Contrary to popular opinion, the function of the cerebellum is not primarily the control of balance although one portion of it is concerned with that factor. The largest portion of the cerebellum sometimes produces a condition in which the afflicted person finds it impossible to reach out his hand toward an object smoothly; instead his hand moves in jerks and exaggerated movements. A small portion of the cerebellum, the *flocculo-nodular lobe,* is concerned with balance. The vestibular portion of the eighth cranial nerve sends some of its fibers to this part of the brain from the semicircular canal portion of the inner ear. Damage to this area of the brain causes loss of balance and dizziness but the person may well adapt himself to the condition and perform almost normally in a short time.

The *medulla* is the lowest part of the brain located at the head of the spinal cord. This is the area controlling heart rate and respiration or breathing, two of the basic needs of the body. The medulla lies just at the base of the skull and extends partially into the bony spinal column. Therefore, an injury at the base of the skull that results in pressure upon the medulla is extremely dangerous and can have serious consequences.

In addition to the general senses the nervous system has a set of special senses; sight, smell, taste, and hearing. These senses originate in organs located in the head—eyes, nose, mouth and ears —and have special or unique ways of getting their information into the central nervous system.

Portions of the nervous systems of all animals are adapted to perform specific actions. In the very simple animals, there are neither eyes nor ears and, so far as we know, nothing like taste or smell. They do have a very sensitive touch reaction, however, and react rapidly and correctly to objects placed in their paths. As animals become more complex, they develop a set of organs to deal specifically with objects. Some react to light, others are sensitive to sound. Some animals have eyes but do not see, since their eyes do not produce a picture of the scene before them, but merely report where there is light. For example, the fresh water mussel and earthworm are sensitive to light but do not see. By moving from one side to the other an animal of this kind can determine where there is light and where there is none. After locating the lighted area, he may either move toward it (in which case he is called *phototropic),* or away from it (in which case he is called *photophobic).* The same type of development occurs with the ear; very simple in elementary animals and becoming more and more complex as the animals become more complex.

The special senses are so called because they deal with stimuli which do not touch the body of the animal to make themselves felt. Without the eyes, for example, we would not know that there is such a thing as light. Without the ears, we would not have the warning of danger, nor the ability to tell where an object fell by the sound it made. However, the notable feature here is that nothing touches the body to deliver this information, yet we sense the presence of light and sound, and are able to act in response to it.

In the case of smell and taste, the situation is somewhat different. The material to be recognized must be either in liquid form or capable of being transformed into a liquid form. Something that is very dry has no taste; all we know is that there is something on the tongue that is rough or smooth. Similarly, when our noses are very dry inside, we cannot smell well. There appears to be a close relationship between taste and smell. When a man has a heavy cold and his nasal passages are blocked, he cannot distinguish odors accurately. At the same time he will experience difficulty in tasting his food. Substances "lose their flavor," we say. You may test this by holding your nose closed with your fingers. Then try to identify the flavor of a variety of foods or liquids. The test can be made stronger by wearing a blindfold at the same time to prevent you from remembering how the food you see should taste when it is taken into the mouth.

SPECIAL SENSE OF SIGHT: The eye is one of the most complex of the sensory organs of the body. It is very delicate, yet amazingly strong. In theory, its activity can be explained very simply but, in actuality, the mechanism is so complex that scientists are not entirely sure how it operates. This is especially true in the field of color vision.

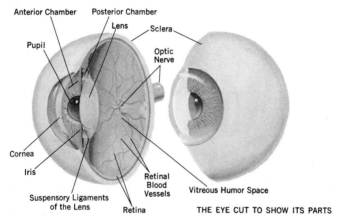

THE EYE CUT TO SHOW ITS PARTS

The eyeball consists of a hollow globe of connective tissue and some muscle. One side of it, the *cornea,* is transparent and admits light into its interior. On the inside, covering almost the entire non-transparent portion of the eyeball, is a layer of specialized, light-sensitive tissue called the *retina.* Between these two parts of the eye are the *lens,* which, like the lens of a camera or magnifying glass, focuses the light on the retina, and the *iris* which controls the amount of light entering the eye cavity by controlling the size of the *pupil.* The iris is pigmented in most people and it is this pigment that produces brown or gray eyes. A lack of pigment produces a blue-eyed person. The iris and lens divide the cavity of the eye into two chambers, an anterior chamber and a posterior chamber. Both of these chambers are kept filled with a liquid called *aqueous humor.* Behind the lens there is another chamber filled with an almost solid, very viscous material called the *vitreous humor*. These two humors are completely transparent. When immersed in water neither material can be detected.

Under normal conditions the eyeball is maintained in an almost constant shape, but an increase or decrease in intraocular fluid pressure occurs in some disease processes and results in a change of shape. The cornea and retina do not change their shape. However, the iris and lens vary. The iris expands and contracts in response to signals from the brain, making the pupil larger or smaller and admitting more or less light into the chambers. The shape of the lens is changed by the action of certain small muscles around its lateral edge, making it thicker or thinner from its anterior or front surface to the posterior or back surface. A thick lens will focus light at a shorter distance behind it than a thin one will. This is helpful when we try to look at an object close to our eyes, and then look at one far away. A camera solves the problem, not by changing the thickness of the lens, but by varying the distance between the lens and the film.

HOW OPTIC NERVE IS FORMED

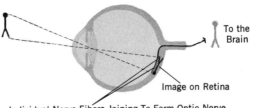

To the Brain

Image on Retina

Individual Nerve Fibers Joining To Form Optic Nerve

When light passes through the cornea and past the iris, it is focused by the lens on the retina, the light-sensitive portion of the eye. The retina, in turn, stimulated by the light, sends an electrochemical message along the *optic nerve* to the brain centers in a similar manner that an impulse reaches the brain from the fingers after touching a hot iron. It is ultimately sent to the posterior part of the cerebral cortex where it is interpreted and recognized as an object having a specific size, shape, color and relationship to its surroundings. At the same time, messages are also sent to subcortical centers in the brain that control or help to control the movement of the head, shoulders, arm and trunk, permitting very rapid, evasive or protective movements in the face of danger. Ducking a baseball suddenly thrown at the head is an example of this type of movement.

We know that we can see a great deal more than the objects immediately in front of the eye. To see an object well we look directly at it, but we can see and recognize things which are not in the central field of vision. This is because we see things best if they are focused on or near the center of the retina, while things focused at the edges of the retina are seen less clearly. A major part of the visual acuteness an animal or man possesses is due to the numbers of cells found in the retina and the distance between them. If there are few cells and they are relatively far apart, only a part of the light pattern (the picture or image) falling on the retina will stimulate individual cells, resulting in a poor picture. The greater the number of cells stimulated per unit area of retina, the sharper a picture will be. Newspaper photographs are printed using a series of black dots to represent the object. The larger the dots, the less definite is the resulting image. On the other hand, very small dots produce a sharp picture.

In the light, two kinds of cells are stimulated, the rods and the cones. *Rod cells* are responsible for black and white vision, while the *cone cells* are sensitive to color. At the center of the retina the rods and cones are very close together and there are more cones than rods. At the peripheral regions or edges, the cones are few and far between, and rods are predominant. Because of the large number of cells at the center part of the retina, definition is best when light is focused there. At the periphery, definition becomes poor since there are fewer cells to be stimulated. At night, cones do not receive enough light to react well, but the rods can act on the amount of light available. Since the cones are found in large numbers in the center of the retina and rods predominate at more peripheral regions, night vision depends on the use of the peripheral parts of the retina. When looking directly at an object in dim light, it often cannot be seen; yet if the eyes are shifted to one side of the object, it can be seen.

VISION

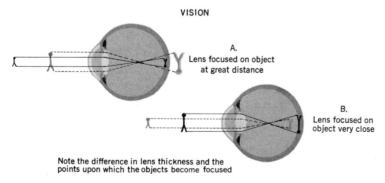

A.
Lens focused on object at great distance

B.
Lens focused on object very close

Note the difference in lens thickness and the points upon which the objects become focused

Since the mechanism of sight partially depends on certain chemically constituted pigments in the retina which must be rebuilt after exposure to light before objects can be seen again in a darker medium, exposure of the eyes to very bright lights before going into dark places results in temporary loss of vision. For instance, if the driver of a car uses "high" or "bright" lights at night and shines them into the eyes of the driver of an oncoming car, he can blind that driver temporarily so that for a few seconds after he goes into the dark again, he cannot clearly see the road ahead.

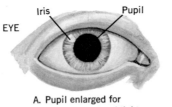
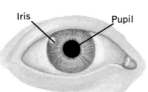

EYE

A. Pupil enlarged for small amounts of light

B. Pupil constricted for large amounts of light

Since these pigments depend chemically upon compounds of the vitamin A family, a man who has a severe vitamin A deficiency may have trouble with his vision, especially at night. Also, any defect or scratch on the surface of the cornea will produce large defects in the objects seen. Because eyes are extremely sensitive instruments and in this modern world we depend on their functioning properly, it makes good sense to take the best possible care of them. They should be checked regularly by a qualified examiner so that any damage that may have resulted from accident or misuse may be corrected as early as possible. Use proper precautions regarding the amount of light used to perform visual tasks such as reading or fine needlework, and keep sharp instruments and tools away from the eyes, always protecting them from flying chips and dust. It does not take much to injure the eyes, but it requires painstaking effort to restore sight once lost.

SPECIAL SENSE OF HEARING: The ear, in contrast to the eye, is in a more protected position, located within the head and having an air passage leading to it. It consists of three major portions: 1. the *external ear,* made up of the cartilaginous flap on the side of the head and the air passage leading to the eardrum (the *external auditory meatus);* 2. the *middle ear,* beginning with the eardrum, having three small bones linked together, and extending from the drum across the middle ear space to a small window in the bone of the skull (the *oval window);* the three bones are called, in order, the *malleus,* the *incus* and the *stapes;* 3. the end or "foot" of the stapes fills the space of the oval window. Inside the bone, beyond the oval window, is the area known as the *inner ear.* This is a set of fluid-filled coiled tubes completely surrounded by bone. Within these tubes is located the arrangement of sound-sensitive membranes and nervous system endings that respond to changes in mechanical pressure.

The ear as a whole is responsive to changes in air pressure as anyone who has ridden in an elevator or an airplane realizes. Sound, traveling through air, is made up of waves of many sizes or amplitudes with varying distances between the tops of the waves. If the distance between wave tops is short, the sound represented is high in pitch but, if the distance is long, the pitch of the sound is low. The distance is often spoken of as the "frequency" of the wave since the shorter the distance, the more waves can pass a given point in a given time. The usual time reference is measured in seconds. Thus middle A on the piano or other musical instrument has a frequency of 440 cycles per second. The higher the wave, the louder will be the sound, and the lower the wave, the softer will be the sound.

When sound waves, traveling through air, enter the external auditory meatus, they travel through it and strike the eardrum. The drum is a very elastic membrane stretched across the end of the passage and can be pushed backward or stretched when it is pushed. Because it is elastic, it tends to return to its original position. Sound waves push the drum back each time they touch it. The drum returns to its original position between waves. This results in vibration of the drum at a rate equal to the frequency of the sound waves striking it. On the other side of the drum, in the middle ear space, the *malleus,* the first of the three ear bones, or *ossicles,* is attached to the drum and moves when the drum moves. Each of the other two bones, the *incus* and the *stapes,* moves when it is pushed by the one ahead of it. The oval foot plate of the stapes in turn pushes on a membrane made of part of the coiled tubes of the inner ear lying in the bone behind the oval window. The fluid in these tubes then is set in motion and shows the same wave form that the original sound wave striking the ear drum had. Thus, the eardrum vibration is transferred to the fluid of the coiled tubes.

There are three tubes lying side-by-side in the coil. The two outer tubes communicate with each other at one end. One of these tubes receives the pressure variations caused by the vibration of the foot of the stapes and transfers them to the other through the communicating hole, the *helicotrema.* The wave then travels down the second tube until it reaches a second small window in the bony wall (the *round window),* and pushes against the membrane stretched

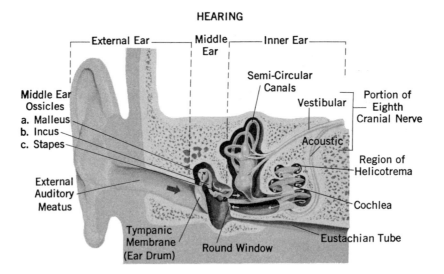

HEARING

External Ear — Middle Ear — Inner Ear

Semi-Circular Canals

Middle Ear Ossicles
a. Malleus
b. Incus
c. Stapes

Vestibular — Portion of Eighth Cranial Nerve

Acoustic

Region of Helicotrema

External Auditory Meatus

Cochlea

Tympanic Membrane (Ear Drum)

Round Window

Eustachian Tube

across it, bulging it out into the middle ear space. The center tube does not communicate with either of the other two directly, but is squeezed or affected by the waves passing through the fluids of these two. By a mechanism which is not understood (although several theories have been proposed to explain the activity), this wave motion changes the conditions inside the middle tube to such an extent that the nerve endings lying between cells in this tube are caused to send messages to the brain. The messages are specific enough to enable the person to recognize a sound of a given frequency up to about 20,000 cycles per second. These messages are carried by the nerve fibers back to the brain and are relayed both upward to the lateral portions of the cerebral cortex where we recognize and identify them, and to centers which control movements of the eyes, the head, the shoulders and trunk so that they may move in response to a sound. For example, a loud sound behind the head and slightly to the left of it results in a louder sound in the left ear than in the right ear. The messages, relayed to the brain, are analyzed and the eyes are turned to the left, together with the head and shoulders, in an effort to locate the source of the sound for further visual identification.

The middle ear space is not entirely closed. It has an air passage connection with the mouth through the *Eustachian tube*. Through this tube, air from the outside of the body can equalize the pressure, either positive or negative, developed within the middle ear space. Thus, when passing from a level of high pressure to one of relatively low pressure, as in going by elevator from the ground floor to the fiftieth floor of a building, the high pressure inside the middle ear space can bleed off through the Eustachian tube and keep the pressures on each side of the eardrum constant. Likewise, when descending from the fiftieth floor to the ground, air can enter the tube and fill the middle ear cavity equalizing the pressure once again. Failure of the equalization system results in unequal pressures on either side of the flexible eardrum and the drum attempts to equalize pressure by being pushed toward the area of low pressure. If the differences in pressure are high enough to force the drum to expand to its elastic limits the drum will rupture or tear, equalizing the pressure, but at the same time making it impossible for it to vibrate and move the ear ossicles. The net result is a marked decrease in hearing ability. Loss of the drum, or even of the ear bones, will not completely abolish hearing: one will not become totally deaf, but hearing will be difficult.

If the Eustachian tube is blocked when postnasal drip resulting from a cold occurs, or if an infection begins in the throat, mouth or nose, and part of the blocking material or infectious matter is forced through the tube from the pharynx into the middle ear cavity by sneezing or coughing, it may well start an infectious process there. Since it is an almost-closed space, warm and moist, it provides a good place for the growth of germs and the formation of pus. Such an inflammation, once well started, will produce pus at a high rate, and it may become necessary to puncture the ear drum to relieve the pressure in order to prevent the drum from suffering damage by tearing or rupture. In some cases, although this was much more common many years ago than it is now, some of the infectious material may be forced by the high pressure within the middle ear cavity proper into a spongy bone area immediately posterior to it. This area is known as the *mastoid bone*. It is an area of bone shot through by many very small air spaces or channels. If an infection begins here, it sometimes is necessary to remove the whole outside surface of this bone in order to remove the infection. Today, such infections are controlled for the most part by antibiotics before they have a chance to become as severe as they did formerly.

Because of the position and vulnerability of the ear drum and ear ossicles, care should be taken that the external auditory meatus is cleaned regularly and with proper attention paid to the cleansing method. The insertion of toothpicks or any other sharp objects into the canal to remove wax should be discouraged. Consult your physician in any case where hearing is diminished on one or both sides, and follow his advice in the matter of regular cleaning. Exposure to very loud or very sharp sounds should be avoided also since in these cases the drum is suddenly put under great strain and may break or tear. It is a good practice, when one must be exposed to such sounds, to keep the mouth open, allowing the pressure on both sides of the drum to be kept at as close to equal pressure as possible.

There is one part of the inner ear that is not usually considered to be a part of the sense of hearing but since it is intimately connected with the cochlea, we will consider it at this point.

Anatomically, the cochlea and the semicircular canals are linked to each other, one being the anatomic extension of the other. The *cochlea* is concerned with hearing sound, while the *semicircular canals* are concerned with the recognition of the position of the head in space. The knowledge of one's position in space is essential for balance.

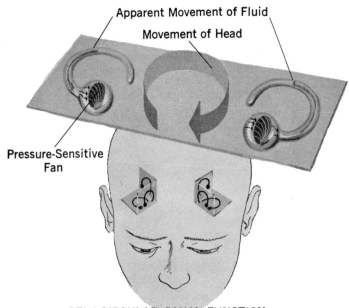

Apparent Movement of Fluid

Movement of Head

Pressure-Sensitive Fan

SEMI-CIRCULAR CANAL FUNCTION

There are three canals on either side of the head. Each set is connected on the same side of the head and shares a connection with the center portion of the cochlea. Individually, they are arranged at 90° angles to each other providing anterior, posterior, and horizontal or inferior reference planes. As a group, the canals are located 45° away from the anterior-posterior line of the head. The canals are fluid-filled, and at one end of the tube a fan shaped object can be found. The fan is anchored to the floor of the tube with its sides lightly fastened to the sides of the tube. The center portion of the fan is flexible, and is bent or pushed by the movement of fluid within the tube. As the head is moved rapidly to the right or left, the tubes, being part of the head, move with the head in the same direction. The fluid tends to stand still while the tube moves, and thus it moves in the opposite direction to the movement of the tube. The fluid exerts a pressure against the flexible fan at the end of the tube as the fan moves, and the fluid appears to move in the opposite direction.

The fan is equipped with nerve endings at its base. These endings are part of the nerve endings of the eighth cranial nerve, the same nerve that supplies the cochlea for hearing. When the fan is bent on one side, the corresponding one in the same plane on the other side of the head is also bent. These two fans, with the nerve endings, begin a series of signals that are sent via the eighth nerve to the brain, and from there to the flocculo-nodular lobe of the cerebellum where the information is interpreted. Data from all the semicircular canals having been received and analyzed, the position of the head can be determined and the result compared to the position of the body and its limbs. Thereby, a total picture of the body's position in space is known, and adjustments can be made when necessary.

SPECIAL SENSE OF TASTE: In the case of the sense of taste, most of the active neuronal elements are located in areas on the surface of the tongue known as *taste buds*. There are others which can be found on the epiglottis and some parts of the wall of the pharynx. These taste buds are composed of groups of specialized cells between which lie the nerve endings that are sensitive to the substances we taste. The mechanism by which the nerve endings are stimulated is not known completely, but it is known that materials to be tasted must be capable of becoming dissolved in a liquid. If very dry materials are placed on the tongue's surface it requires a

LOCATION OF THE SENSITIVE ORGANS
OF TASTE AND SMELL

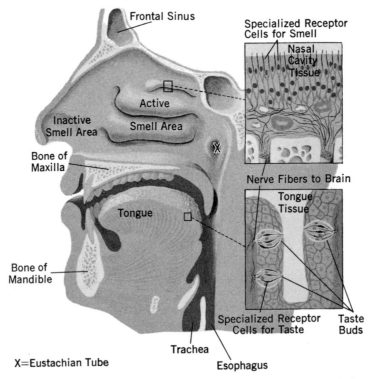

X=Eustachian Tube

rather long time before we "taste" them, certainly long enough for them to become wetted by our saliva and to dissolve partially. Breathing through the mouth for long periods of time, as is some- times necessary at the dentist's office, results in a dry mouth. That is, the membranes of the mouth and tongue dry off faster than saliva can moisten them. Under this condition it takes some time before anything can be tasted at all. Even water when taken into the mouth does not taste as water does under more normal conditions.

Temperature also has its effect on the sense of taste. Very hot or very cold liquids are not tasted immediately, but must wait for the lowering or raising of the liquid's temperature to one more nearly equal to that of the mouth and tongue.

There appear to be specialized areas of taste; that is, areas that are sensitive to special types of taste such as sweet, sour, acid, etc. It is also true that when the taste buds have been subjected to strong stimuli, they must in a sense "rest" awhile before they are fully capable of interpreting a weak stimulus.

THE SPECIAL SENSE OF SMELL: The nose, with its sense of smell, is closely associated with the tongue and its sense of taste. The active elements in both are special nerve fiber endings located in the moist exposed surface inside the nose and in the wet surface of the tongue. In order for either to be felt, the material to be smelled or tasted must be dissolved in a fluid and come into some sort of contact with the nerve endings or sensitive elements.

The nose has a number of parts. The portion of the nasal cavity immediately inside the nose is called the *vestibule*. This portion is not usually sensitive to smell. Behind the vestibule is the area which is sensitive to odors. From the lateral sides of the chamber or nasal cavity three bony projections called *turbinate* bones hang down into the cavity. These are covered with a mucous membrane similar to that covering the rest of the tract. As air is drawn through the nose it comes into contact with the wet surface of the membrane and the odoriferous material comes into contact with the nerve endings between the cells of the membrane. These nerve endings select the information presented to them and send messages upward by means of their fibers to pass through the floor of the skull to a portion of the brain known as the *olfactory bulb,* located just over the eye. From this point the information is relayed backward to the rest of the brain and is sent, among other places, to the lateral part of the cerebral cortex where we recognize whether the particular odor is agreeable or disagreeable. Just how the endings in the nasal mucosa are selective about the information which they transmit is not known. A great deal of work is being done in an attempt to discover the mechanism but, at present, dependable information is scant.

Chapter Five

RESPIRATORY SYSTEM

When considering the respiratory system, one usually thinks of it as comprising the trachea and the lungs alone. It does, however, have as part of it the mouth, the nose, and the pharynx. The system is primarily a way of getting a certain volume of air into contact with a portion of the blood stream so that oxygen and carbon dioxide can be exchanged within the body. Oxygen is needed by all the tissues of the body for the life of the individual cells and for their work. Carbon dioxide is the most common by-product of that work and must be passed off before the cells become poisoned.

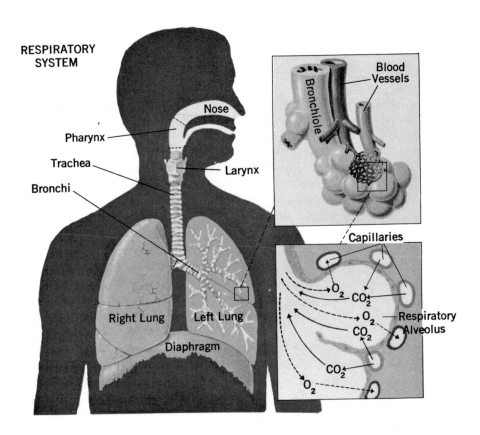

RESPIRATORY SYSTEM

Nose

Pharynx

Trachea

Bronchi

Larynx

Right Lung

Left Lung

Diaphragm

Bronchiole

Blood Vessels

Capillaries

O_2 CO_2

O_2 CO_2 — Respiratory Alveolus

CO_2

O_2

It is passed into the blood stream where it combines with the hemoglobin of the blood and is carried to the capillaries of the lungs. At this point the carbon dioxide is exchanged for the oxygen and is expired into the surrounding atmosphere as waste material. The oxygen is carried back to the tissues by the blood stream and delivered to the cells of the body through their own capillaries for their use.

The respiratory system is only a means to an end. All mammals have approximately the same system, consisting of a mouth and nose connected through the pharynx with the trachea, and ending in the lungs. Insects, on the other hand, have no lungs as we know them. Instead, they are provided with a series of small holes or sacs along the sides of their bodies. These sacs can be filled with air and then closed off, the oxygen passing through the inner walls of the sac into the blood stream while the carbon dioxide passes out into it. When the air is used up (becomes depleted of its oxygen), the holes or sacs are opened and the waste gases are expired and replaced by a new supply. Some of the water insects such as the water-boatmen (Corixidae) even carry bubbles of air next to the surfaces of their bodies in contact with the sacs and use it while they swim about under water. These are all examples of one process—the provision of a mechanism for acquiring oxygen and getting rid of carbon dioxide.

The nose or mouth, pharynx, trachea, and bronchial tree are simply tubes which provide a route to the functional part of the system. At the end of the bronchial tree are a large number of very small, thin-walled pockets or sacs. These are air-filled when we take a deep breath. Just outside the thin walls of these sacs are complex nets of capillaries carrying blood which has been collected from all over the body by the veins, and pumped through the capillaries of the lung by the pulmonary arteries from the heart. The oxygen from the air sacs and the carbon dioxide from the blood stream must pass through the walls of the sac and the capillary on their way to their final destination.

When we take a deep breath, we often take into our lungs other matter besides the oxygen we need. For example, in dry areas there is the road dust kicked up by cars or trucks; in the mines, tiny particles of coal and stone; in mills, the lint and even minute particles of steel from sawing or cutting machines. All these particles enter the lung along with the air we breathe. Some particles are deposited along the way to the lungs on the mucous-lined surfaces of the trachea and bronchial tubes, from which they are gradually moved back toward the mouth and are finally spat out. Other particles reach the functional portions of the lungs, the air sacs, and are deposited on their surfaces. If they form a heavy coat over these surfaces, air cannot pass across the wall to the blood stream, and the body cannot get the oxygen it needs. (Water in these air sacs produces this same condition, and drowning results because oxygen cannot be delivered to the tissues of the body.) If the particles are sharp, such as those made of stone, coal or steel, they may cut the walls of the sacs. The cuts are small, and taken by themselves are not very dangerous. It is only when there have been a great many of these small cuts, repeated often, one day after another, that they become dangerous. Each time the surface of an organ is cut, it must heal itself and healing of a cut or an abrasion involves the development of scar tissue. Scar tissue is relatively tough and impervious to the passage of gases and, in most tissues of the body, this is a valuable characteristic. The lungs, however, depend on their ability to pass gases across their walls, and the rest of the tissues of the body gradually suffocate without the oxygen they need to survive.

Fortunately, the prevention of this type of disorder is fairly simple. Whenever working in areas or atmospheres where dust, lint, or particulate matter is suspended in the air, wearing a light dust mask or respirator with filters designed to take this dust out of the air, will remove the cause and prevent the disease that might follow as a result.

Smoking of course, introduces a somewhat similar problem since tobacco smoke, when inhaled, carries with it certain amounts of nicotine and tar. In sufficient quantities these materials act as destructive agents on the lung tissues. It has been claimed that the tars which are derived from tobacco can cause cancer. This has been demonstrated in experimental animals, and by statistical analysis of men and women who smoke. It is generally true that many compounds not ordinarily found in the air supply necessary for life, can cause severe disorders of respiration, and even poisoning if they are present in sufficient concentration. In the case of tobacco, its resulting in cancer of the lung seems to be dependent upon the amount of smoke inhaled by the smoker, and possibly a latent predisposition to cancer of the lung in a smoker. At present, there is no way of evaluating an individual's predisposition or lack of it.

CIRCULATORY SYSTEM

The heart is the central figure in the circulatory system, and without it the whole system will not work. While the veins, arteries and capillaries must be functionally operative, the heart is the mainspring.

SEQUENCE OF HEART CHAMBER ACTION

Darkest tint represents oxygenated blood   Medium tint represents non-oxygenated blood

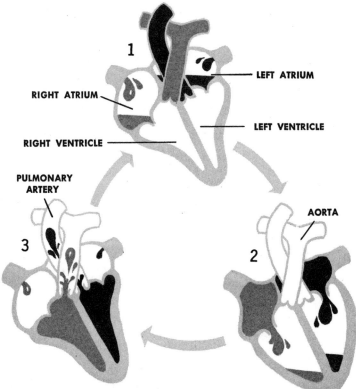

RIGHT ATRIUM

LEFT ATRIUM

LEFT VENTRICLE

RIGHT VENTRICLE

PULMONARY ARTERY

AORTA

1. The two atria receive blood from the body (right atrium; non-oxygenated blood) and the lungs (left atrium; oxygenated blood).

2. The atria contract and the valves relax allowing blood to flow into the two ventricles.

3. The ventricular musculature contracts, forcing oxygenated blood from the left ventricle into the aorta (to the body in general) and non-oxygenated blood from the right ventricle into the pulmonary artery (to the lungs).

As we have said while discussing muscle tissue, the heart is a special form of general striated muscle. It has neither bone nor skeletal system to support it, gets very little rest in comparison to other muscles, and works harder and longer than almost any other part of the body. In form it is hollow, having four chambers—two on top and two on the bottom. The two top chambers, the *atria,* receive the blood coming to the heart from other parts of the body, while the two bottom chambers, the *ventricles,* send blood out to the rest of the body. The atria are connected to the ventricles directly and communicate with them through sets of valves. The right atrium lies directly over the right ventricle and communicates with it via the *tricuspid valve.* The left atrium lies directly over the left ventricle and communicates with it via the *bicuspid valve.* These valves are thin sheets of tough connective tissue, anchored on one side against the walls of the heart between the atrium and ventricle, while the free edge projects into the space or cavity of the heart itself. This free edge is anchored by tough threads of the same material to masses or columns of muscle *(papillary muscle)* found on the walls and base of the ventricular space. Thus blood entering the atrium from the veins fills and expands its relatively thin muscular walls. After a short time the atrial muscle contracts and pushes the blood through the valve space into the ventricle, expands its thick muscular walls, and fills the ventricular cavity. While the blood is flowing past the valves, it pushes the valve leaves flat against the walls of the ventricle. When sufficient blood has entered the ventricle to begin to flow upward behind the valve leaves, the leaves begin to rise and start to close. With the contraction of the ventricular musculature, the blood is forced upward in a greater degree. The valve leaves are pushed ahead of it until the free edge of each leaf reaches the limit of travel allowed by the cords or threads running from the free edge to the papillary muscles. These leaves are so arranged that when they have reached a position about midway between the atrium and the ventricle, the edges meet. The edges are slightly thickened and, when pressed closely together, prevent the passage of blood from the atrium back into the ventricle. Instead, the blood is pushed out of the ventricles through the appropriate artery to be distributed to the proper area.

Some people refer to the "right" and "left" hearts; that is, the right atrium and the right ventricle form the "right heart," while the left atrium and left ventricle form the "left heart." In the right heart, the atrium receives all the blood returning to the heart from the entire body except the lungs and passes it to the right ventricle which then pushes it out of the heart to the lungs where gas exchange takes place. In the left heart, the atrium receives all the blood returning to the heart from the lungs, passes it in turn to the left ventricle which then pushes it out of the heart into the *aorta,* the major artery carrying oxygenated blood to the tissues of the entire body. Together, since the two halves of the heart, or right and left hearts, operate at exactly the same time, the muscular contractions of the chambers provide the energy to move blood throughout the body.

After being forced out of the left ventricle into the aorta, a large elastic blood vessel which expands under the pressure of the liquid pushed into it, the blood begins its journey through the body. A small set of valves, the *aortic valves* located at the junction of the aorta and the left ventricle snap shut, thus preventing the blood from returning to the ventricle when the pressure is released. The aortic walls, having been expanded by the incoming blood from the heart, now begin to return to their normal shape and size. This applies a steady pressure against the blood contained within the aorta and forces it to move along the vessel and into the branches of it to be distributed to the various specific parts of the body. We feel a strong pulse beat at the wrist when the heart muscle contracts, but we do not feel the steady pressure exerted by the aorta unless we use the type of machine designed to measure blood pressure.

Moving through the aorta and its branches, the blood travels through progressively smaller and smaller vessels, all arteries, until it gets to the smallest of them. These are called *capillaries* and a collection of them is termed a *capillary bed*. Capillaries, thin-walled tubes whose walls are only one cell thick and have no muscle, are surrounded by a very thin layer of connective tissue. They are found in all the tissues of the body and lie between the cells of muscles, the liver, the kidneys, the stomach, and just under the surface of the skin; in fact, in every place one can look. Through the thin walls of these vessels the exchange of oxygen and food materials for carbon dioxide and other waste products takes place. In the lungs, the waste products are exchanged through capillary walls for the oxygen drawn into the air spaces of the lung. These spaces are called *the alveoli*.

During its passage through the capillary bed, the blood loses most of its food materials and oxygen and picks up waste products excreted by the cells of the tissues. It then begins to leave the capillaries, which join together and form larger and larger veins, finally emptying into the largest of the veins, the *vena cava* which returns it to the right atrium of the heart. The cycle has now been completed.

The heart rate, the number of beats per minute, is determined by the fact that it is responsible for delivering a certain amount

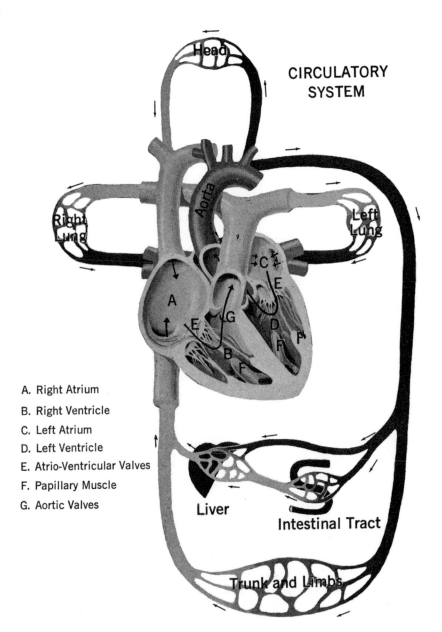

CIRCULATORY
SYSTEM

A. Right Atrium
B. Right Ventricle
C. Left Atrium
D. Left Ventricle
E. Atrio-Ventricular Valves
F. Papillary Muscle
G. Aortic Valves

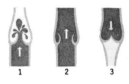

ACTION OF VALVES IN THE VEINS
Arrow shows direction of blood flow

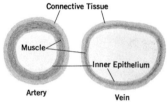

DIFFERENCES IN THE THICKNESS OF
THE WALLS OF ARTERIES AND VEINS

of oxygenated blood to the tissues and getting rid of a certain amount of waste material in a unit of time. During periods of low physical activity, such as when we are asleep, the body does not require so much oxygen nor produce so much carbon dioxide as it does when we are working hard. The circulatory system is equipped with a built-in chemical detector just above the heart. This detector responds to the amount of oxygen and carbon dioxide in the blood passing by, and sends a message to the brain via the sensory nerve fibers that end in it. Once this message has been received and interpreted, the brain responds by slowing down or speeding up the heart rate to supply more or less blood to the tissues and also by increasing or decreasing the breathing rate in order to adjust the supply of oxygen available to the blood stream in the capillaries of the lungs. Thus, when a man is sleeping, his heart beats very slowly and his breathing rate is correspondingly slow while they become much more rapid when he is doing physical work. In time of emotional stress or when one is disturbed or angry, the heart rate is also speeded up in order to provide the energy necessary to cope with the problem at hand.

Although the heart helps to deliver food materials to the rest of the body, the heart itself, being constructed of muscle, must have its own supplies of these materials also. The blood filling the heart chambers is not ordinarily available to the muscle of the heart, since the interior of the chambers is covered by a protective covering or epithelium that prevents the blood from reaching the muscle fibers. To supply the necessary materials, therefore, the heart must depend on the same artery-capillary-vein network found in the rest of the body.

These arteries and veins are called the *coronary vessels*. The arteries receive blood from the aorta just above the aortic valves and distribute it through the capillary bed of the heart to the individual heart muscle fibers. The exchange of food materials and oxygen for waste products and carbon dioxide is made at this point. Blood then passes into the small venous vessels that in turn empty into the coronary veins, returning it to the right atrium where it is mixed with venous blood returning from the rest of the body.

The coronary circulation, in its general pattern, is not much different from the circulation of other parts of the body. However, the muscles of other parts of the body work for a time and then have an opportunity to rest, but the heart is constantly working with only very short rest periods between individual beats. The heart's circulation must be of the best, therefore, constant and without interruption. Unfortunately, once in a while a small blood clot traveling through the circulatory system will become lodged in one of the vessels of the heart blocking the flow of blood to that part of the heart. Deprived of its blood supply, this portion of the heart's muscle is seriously crippled and may die. If the damage is slight, the rest of the heart will continue to operate without too much difficulty but, if the damage is great, the heart may be unable to function and the person may die.

The pain resulting from damage to the heart muscle is Nature's way of reporting that something has happened which requires help and rest in order to remedy the condition. Pain may also result from irritation of nerve fibers in the chest wall. This pain (pleurisy) is sometimes confused with the pain of heart damage, but in either case the safe reaction to pain in the left chest and arm is to visit a doctor for a complete checkup.

Chapter Seven

TEETH

The teeth develop in the mouth, or actually in the jaws, in close association with the development of the bone of the jaws, but are not bone themselves. When the embryo has reached the point where the jaws are fully formed in shape, and the bones of the jaws are about to begin to form, the epithelium of the mouth begins to show thickening in its surface, bulging downward toward the lower jawbone (mandible) and upward toward the bone of the upper

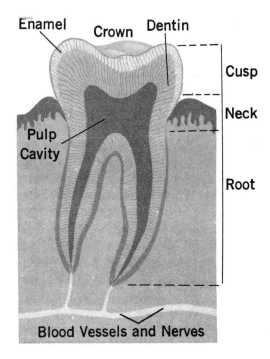

TOOTH CUT TO EXPOSE INTERNAL STRUCTURE

jaw (maxilla). These thickenings soon move away from the surface and form a stocking cap-like structure, with the point of the
cap directed toward the epithelial surface and the rim of the cap
toward the bone. Inside this cap structure or "tooth bud," the
structure of the tooth starts to take shape.

A special group of cells begins to form the *enamel* of the
tooth as the outer shell, while another group forms the *dentin* just
underneath the enamel. Inside the dentin, which is softer than
enamel, but harder than most other tissues of the body, lies the
pulp of the tooth. The pulp is the area in which the nerves, blood
vessels, and their supporting connective tissues lie. A cavity in a
tooth usually begins as a break or crack in the enamel and, if it
enlarges, it penetrates into the dentin. Then one feels pain associated with the cavity, and if the cavity enlarges sufficiently to reach
the pulp of the tooth, all the structures that support the life of the
tooth may be severly affected and die. The dangerous part of leaving cavities unattended lies in the fact that the pulp of the tooth
receives its blood vessels and nerves through a channel common to
all the teeth in that jaw. If an infection begins in the pulp of one
tooth, and spreads through the rest of that tooth into the common
channel, an abscess may form between the root and the socket in
which the tooth is held. It may also spread through the channel
affecting the other teeth on that side and causing destruction of the
bone of that jaw. This, if not attended to soon enough, will cause
the loss of the affected teeth and serious damage to the bone of
the jaw.

Babies are not born with teeth but teeth are in the process of
development inside the jaws. These first teeth are the *deciduous
teeth*. They are also called "baby" or "milk teeth." Several months
after birth these teeth begin to push upward toward the surface of
the mouth. As they grow upward the roots are formed below them
until the tooth has erupted and is visible on the surface within the
mouth. There are already present the early developments of the
permanent dentition which will appear later in life.

The *permanent teeth* begin their development underneath or
beside the deciduous teeth. They are formed in the same manner as
the deciduous teeth and as they grow larger and longer, the root
systems of the deciduous teeth are gradually resorbed and dis-
appear. When the deciduous teeth fall out or are pulled out in
order to make room for the permanent teeth, they often consist of
nothing more than the enamel and dentin of the crown, that portion which is seen within the mouth.

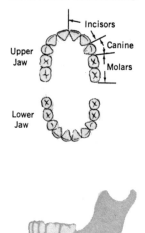

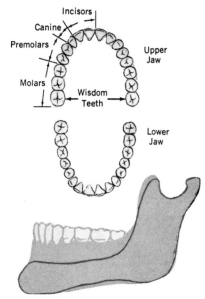

Deciduous Teeth and Appearance
of a Child's Mandible

Permanent Teeth and Appearance of an Adult's Mandible.
The dark outline shows the shape of the Mandible following
loss of teeth and consequent bone resorption.

The bone of the jaws also changes during this period and continues to change throughout life. The bone grows in size and becomes heavier as the embryo grows and as the child grows to adult size. It changes its shape to accommodate itself to the presence or absence of the teeth that it supports. If a tooth grows into the mouth improperly and is twisted out of the normal line, the dentist may apply a brace designed to force it to change its position and become straight. This takes time since the bone of the jaw forming the base of the socket must change its shape in order to allow the tooth to alter its position. The procedure is usually used with teenagers when the permanent teeth appear in order to straighten them or to fill too large gaps between teeth. However, it can also be done in the mouths of older persons. It demonstrates the fact that bone, and in this case the bone of the jaws, is continually being altered to fit the conditions under which it is being used. The cycle is complete when, after all the teeth have been lost by dental extraction or decay, the jaws respond to the situation by becoming much shorter in height. The bone of the upper and lower jaws nearest the mouth and surrounding the teeth supports the teeth; so when the teeth are gone, and no substitute has been made for them, that bone is resorbed and disappears, apparently because it no longer has anything to do.

Anatomy

44

Dental care is extremely important because diseases of the mouth and gums, and decay of the teeth, often cause symptoms of pain and disorder in other parts of the body. Since it is almost impossible for persons other than dentists to recognize the signs of tooth decay, it is necessary to have the teeth checked as often as possible on a regular schedule (usually every six months to one year). If decay and minor erosions of the teeth are found early, they can be repaired without much trouble or expense, but if neglected too long they may develop into serious problems which require time and money to alleviate, not to mention the discomfort of having the work done!

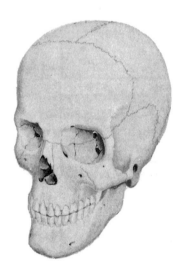

Chapter Eight

DIGESTIVE SYSTEM

When one speaks of the digestive system most people think only of the stomach and the intestinal tract. Actually, the digestive tract is composed of the mouth, with the salivary glands, the esophagus, the stomach, the duodenum with the associated liver and gall bladder together with the pancreas, the rest of the small intestine (the ileum and the jejunum), the large intestine (the colon) with its appendix at the junction of the small and large intestines, and the rectum. Each of these has a specific part to play in the intake and preparation of the food we eat or in the elimination of the waste products of that food.

The entire digestive system consists of a long tube open to the outside of the body on either end. The tube has a different size and shape in each of its various sections, but it is essentially the same tube modified in these sections for specific purposes. It consists of a number of layers wrapped one around another to form

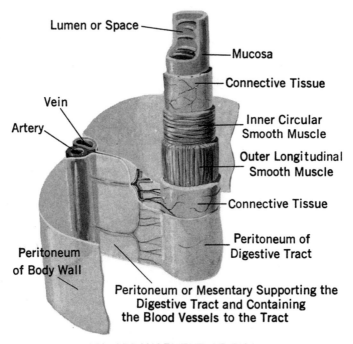

Lumen or Space

Mucosa

Connective Tissue

Vein

Artery

Inner Circular Smooth Muscle

Outer Longitudinal Smooth Muscle

Connective Tissue

Peritoneum of Body Wall

Peritoneum of Digestive Tract

Peritoneum or Mesentary Supporting the Digestive Tract and Containing the Blood Vessels to the Tract

TYPICAL ARRANGEMENT OF TISSUES
IN THE DIGESTIVE TRACT

the full tube. The inside layer, the mucosal layer, is formed by an inner coating of cells called the *epithelium,* supported by a connective tissue layer. The latter ties the epithelium to the muscle layers beneath it and also carries the blood vessels, which are responsible for transferring the food materials picked up by the epithelium, to the liver and to the rest of the body.

The digestive process begins with the mouth. The mouth, together with the teeth and salivary glands, form the first part of the digestive system. Here food is introduced into the body, bitten off by the teeth, chewed to a finer consistency, and moistened by the saliva. Saliva has within it several chemical agents known as *enzymes.* These enzymes have the ability to begin the breakdown of complex molecules into much simpler ones, or to change a compound from one form into another that is useable somewhere else. The salivary enzymes begin the digestive process by starting to change starches into sugars. This is continued as the food passes from the mouth into the esophagus and is carried to the stomach.

From the mouth the food (now called a *bolus* by scientists) is passed through the pharynx and into the esophagus. The esophagus is merely a tube of muscle and connective tissue joining the pharynx with the stomach. It is quite flexible and can be expanded or stretched by the bolus of food passing through it. In periods between swallows it is collapsed and pressed back against the vertebral column by the trachea and the large muscle masses in front of it. It lies downward behind the heart and between the lungs. The lower end of it passes through the diaphragm and ends in the cardiac portion (the upper end) of the stomach.

When the food has reached the stomach the digestive process begun in the mouth is continued. Again it is wetted, this time by a fluid secretion of the walls of the stomach itself, and it is "churned" into a semi-liquid mass by the action of the muscle walls of this organ. The fluid, called gastric juice, is a combination of certain enzymes and hydrochloric acid in water. The acid is useful in breaking down large fat molecules into smaller ones more easily utilized in the next section of the tract, the duodenum. Pepsin, produced by some of the cells of the stomach walls, is also helpful in this process. Acid is apparently necessary to provide the stimulus for opening the valve between the stomach and the duodenum, for when the food mass has been wetted and made sufficiently acid, the valve opens and the mass is forced out of the stomach into the duodenum.

This portion of the digestive tract is rather short but it is here

DIGESTIVE SYSTEM

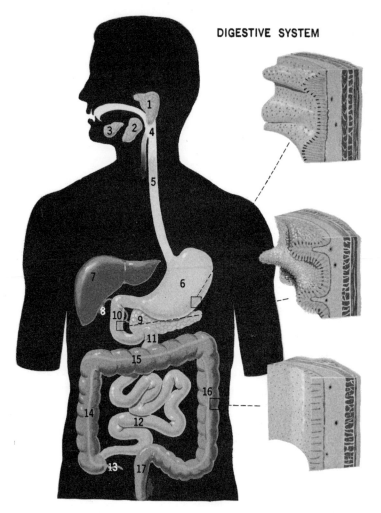

1. Parotid Gland	The Small Intestine	The Large Intestine
2. Submaxillary Gland	10. Duodenum	14. Ascending Colon
3. Sublingual Gland	11. Jejunum	15. Transverse Colon
The Salivary Glands	12. Ileum	16. Descending Colon
4. Pharynx	13. Appendix	17. Rectum
5. Esophagus		
6. Stomach		
7. Liver		
8. Gall Bladder		
9. Pancreas		

The enlarged squares show the microscopic appearance of the wall of the organ from which they were taken. Note the adaptations for increased surface area.

that the major part of digestion takes place. For this reason, it is a very important part of the tract. Opening into it are the stomach, the liver and gall bladder and a part of the pancreas. In addition to the secretions of these organs, the duodenum produces many compounds necessary to the complete preparation of food materials for use. It also provides some compounds that stimulate the liver, the gall bladder, and the pancreas to release their secretions to complete the job.

In the duodenum complex food materials are transformed into simple ones that the body is able to absorb and use. The duodenum is also the site of the first major absorption of the food materials thus produced. Absorption takes place through the walls of the organ. The greater the wall area in contact with the food material, the larger will be the amount absorbed, and the wall of the duodenum has a special modification to increase its wall area. Folds of the mucous membrane facing the inside of the duodenum project into the *lumen,* or passageway, increasing the effective surface. In addition, on the folds and walls of the duodenum, there are a large number of very small projections, called *villi,* which increase the effective absorbing surface, making it possible to transfer large amounts of food materials from the lumen of the duodenum, through the cells of the wall of the organ, into the blood vessels lying behind those walls.

After passing through the duodenum, the food mass continues into the rest of the small intestine, more material being absorbed from the mass as it passes downward. By the time it reaches the colon most of the useable food materials have been removed. During passage of the mass through the colon, water is removed, and the mass is concentrated into a solid form rather than a liquid one.

At the junction of the small and large intestines and attached to the lower end of the large intestine is the appendix which is found in the lower right portion of the abdominal cavity. This organ enjoys a bad reputation for two reasons; it develops acute inflammations at times and must be surgically removed (appendectomy), and its function in the normal human body is not known. A person can get along very well without the appendix. Its removal causes no trouble with digestion, and its presence does not seem to aid it. However, removal of a normal appendix, simply because it might cause trouble later, is not recommended by reputable authorities. Such procedure would be similar to having one's teeth pulled because they might develop cavities and cause trouble later.

Chapter Nine

URINARY SYSTEM

The urinary system, like most of the other systems of the body, is composed of a number of parts. It begins with the kidneys, one on the right side and one on the left, which empty into a tube called the *ureter*. The ureter, in turn, empties into the *bladder* and the bladder discharges the urine through the *urethra*. The system is the same in both the male and the female.

The kidneys are the functional unit; that is, it is in the kidneys that urine is produced. The remaining parts of the system merely carry the urine from the kidneys to an area where it can be stored to be discharged at the proper time. Where does urine come from? At the *hilus,* the point of entry of the kidney, is an artery entering it. This artery supplies small branches called arterial capillaries to structures called *glomeruli*. In the basket-shaped glomerulus, the capillaries are formed into a small ball, which is shaped like the rubber threads inside a golf ball. Blood passes through the capillaries under high pressure and, at this pressure, the liquids of the blood stream leak through the walls of the vessels, leaving the cells and proteins behind. The liquid, having left the capillaries, finds itself in what is known as *Bowman's capsule,* the structure that forms the wall of the glomerulus. It flows into the space between the capillary wall and the wall of the capsule and from there into the tube leading away from the capsule. The tube is quite long and varies in diameter from one end to the other, being large at first, then narrow, and then large again. The first part of the tube and the last part are tortuous and coiled and lie close to the glomerulus. The middle section is long and straight and stretches quite a distance away from the glomerulus before it returns to it. The tube is surrounded by the continuation of the capillaries in the glomerulus.

As the fluid makes its way down the tube from the glomerulus, it comes into contact with the walls of the tube, and portions of the liquid are taken back from the tube and passed to the capillaries again. Thus sugars, certain amounts of ions like sodium and potassium, and other materials are returned to the blood stream to be used elsewhere in the body. The materials that are not taken back through the walls of the tube are allowed to continue through it. The water is also removed from the tube in large quantities. In this way the water content of the body is preserved. Without this function, the body would require a constant intake of water in order to sustain life.

KIDNEY WITH ENLARGEMENT OF ONE OF THE FUNCTIONAL UNITS

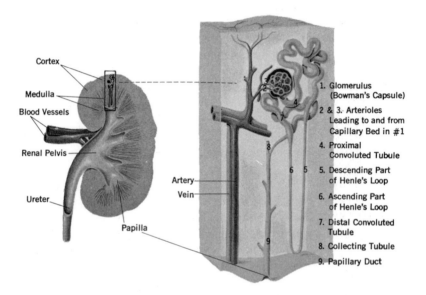

Cortex
Medulla
Blood Vessels
Renal Pelvis
Ureter
Papilla
Artery
Vein

1. Glomerulus (Bowman's Capsule)
2 & 3. Arterioles Leading to and from Capillary Bed in #1
4. Proximal Convoluted Tubule
5. Descending Part of Henle's Loop
6. Ascending Part of Henle's Loop
7. Distal Convoluted Tubule
8. Collecting Tubule
9. Papillary Duct

Having reached the end of the tube, the fluid (provisional urine) enters another tube called the collecting tubule and passes downward to empty into the large space at the hilus of the kidney. At this point, the ureter is attached to the hilus, and the fluid collected from all the glomeruli that are working passes into it and downward to the bladder.

The bladder is a small, distensible sac lying just behind the pubic bones of the pelvis, and is equipped with a series of layers of smooth muscle. When the bladder is receiving urine through the ureters, it slowly expands under the fluid pressure, stretching the smooth muscle layers of its walls. These muscle fibers, like those of the skeletal muscles of the arms and legs, have a set of nerve fibers attached to them. Both sensory and motor fibers are present. When the muscle fibers have reached a certain degree of stretch, the sensory nerve fibers signal to the spinal cord that the bladder is almost full and that it is time to empty it. The information is transferred up the spinal cord to the brain and we become consciously aware of the condition. At the same time, the spinal cord reacts to this sensory information by slight contraction of the smooth muscle of the bladder to begin the process of elimination of urine.

In most people that process cannot be completed, however, until we consciously act upon the information received in the brain. Below the bladder and surrounding the urethra, the tube leading from the bladder to the exterior, are two sets of muscles known as *sphincters* or *constrictors*. These muscles are normally kept in a state of contraction and close the urethra to the passage of urine from the bladder. If they were to remain relaxed and the urethra remained open, urine would slowly leave the bladder and, running through the urethra, would leak out of the body continuously. At the proper time, the brain sends motor information to the lower part of the spinal cord, the muscles or sphincters are relaxed, and the smooth muscle of the bladder actively contracts to force urine out of the bladder.

Since the bladder is connected to the exterior by a short tube, it is somewhat liable to infection. Concretions or "stones" may be formed in the bladder or the hilus of the kidney. These afflictions are very painful and are felt most acutely in the process of elimination of urine. A doctor's advice and examination should be obtained as soon as pain is felt in the region of the bladder or the back just under the rib cage.

Endocrine or "ductless" glands take their names from the fact that they secrete their products (hormones) and discharge them into the bloodstream rather than into the digestive tract or other cavity of the body. The bloodstream then carries these secretions through the body until they are deposited in the organs where they are able to do their work. Not all organs or tissues of the body can be affected by endocrine gland secretions. The tissues that can be affected are often called the "target organs."

There are eight major endocrine glands in the human body. They are: the pineal gland, the pituitary gland, the thyroid gland, the parathyroid gland, the thymus, the pancreas (endocrine portion), the adrenal glands and the testes or ovaries.

The function of the endocrine glands is the regulation of certain activities of the body concerned with its form, shape, physical constitution, and metabolic activity. This type of regulation may be contrasted with that exerted by the nervous system which enables one to walk, run, move arms and legs at will, or in a particular manner and speeds up the heart and breathing rate. In other words, while the nervous system exerts its control immediately for quick response and then relaxes, the endocrine gland system exerts its control over relatively long periods of time, and the changes produced are slow but profound.

The *pineal gland,* or *pineal body,* is a portion of the brain. It lies deep between the two hemispheres and is an outpouching of the center portion of the brain. Its function is not known. Although in young people it is glandular in appearance and structure, as one grows older it often hardens and becomes stony.

The *pituitary gland,* on the other hand, while also in close association with the brain, has activities which are well known. This gland is derived partly from the epithelium of the mouth and partly from an outpouching of the base of the brain. In very early development of the embryo, a small pouch of cells lining the pharynx sinks into the roof of the pharynx and detaches itself from the mouth entirely. It makes its way upward to become wrapped around another outpouching from the base of the brain. Thus the pituitary gland is formed. Those portions derived from the pharynx are called the anterior and intermediate lobes, while the part derived from the brain is called the neural lobe. Most of the information on the function of the pituitary gland is concerned with the anterior lobe.

The pituitary has been called the "master" gland because, by its action, most of the other endocrine glands are stimulated to act or are depressed. The action of the pituitary itself controls the rate of growth of the body, and too little or too much of the hormone used for this purpose may produce a dwarf or a giant. The other hormones produced by the gland control the thyroid gland, the adrenal gland, and the testes or ovaries. Without these hormones, the organs mentioned will operate at a very low level, if at all.

The *thyroid gland* lies over the trachea and larynx in the neck. It is this gland that controls the rate at which the body uses its food materials. Stimulated by the pituitary to produce its own hormone, the thyroid can speed up that rate and then control it, so that metabolism can proceed at the proper level. Without enough thyroid hormone the body's metabolic rate falls to a lower level and the person becomes slow and sluggish throughout. He may also gain a great deal of weight, since the food that he eats is not used but stored instead. Too much thyroid hormone speeds up the rate, and the person may lose weight, become extremely nervous, irritable, and restless.

The thyroid gland depends on the presence of iodine in the diet to perform properly. If iodine is not present, the thyroid may enlarge greatly, producing a large bulge (a goiter) in the neck over the trachea. In the past this disease was common in areas where the people had no access to salt-water fish or seaweeds. At present the availability of iodized salt for table use has greatly reduced its occurrence.

On either side of the posterior surfaces of the thyroid gland and embedded in it are four smaller glands. These are called the *parathyroid glands*. They are responsible for the control and proper use of calcium. Their removal causes a lowering of the amount of calcium found in the bloodstream and death may follow. On the other hand, too much calcium will also lead to death. It is believed that the parathyroids control the amount of calcium in the skeleton. The mechanism of this deposition is not fully understood at present.

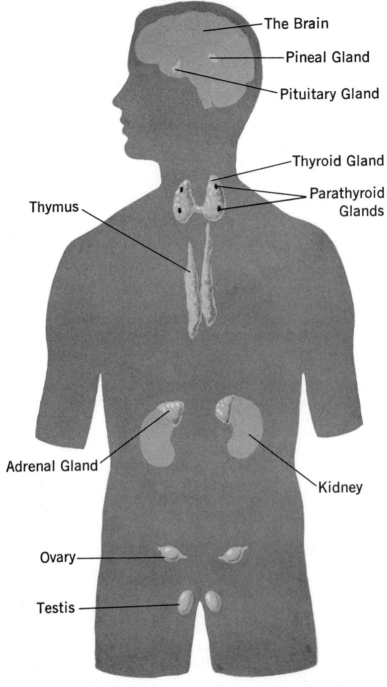

The Brain

Pineal Gland

Pituitary Gland

Thyroid Gland

Parathyroid Glands

Thymus

Adrenal Gland

Kidney

Ovary

Testis

GLANDS

The *thymus gland* is located in the upper part of the chest, lying over the trachea under the first several ribs. Its function is not certain although it appears to be active during childhood and gradually regresses and becomes smaller as growth reaches its limit.

The endocrine portion of *the pancreas* is responsible for regulating the amount of sugar in the body. To do this it produces a hormone called *insulin* which makes available to the body, in a form it can use, the sugar which is taken into the body. In the absence of insulin, the sugar is excreted in the urine without being used. This condition is called *diabetes mellitus*. A diabetic person can control his condition by the injection of insulin into his body by hypodermic, thereby restoring the ability to utilize the sugar instead of excreting it.

The *adrenal glands* take their name from the fact that they are found on top of the kidneys (ad-renal or to the kidney). These glands are responsible for the regulation, among other things, of the amounts of sodium and potassium present in the bloodstream. Without these important chemicals, the nervous system will not function and cells of other parts of the body lose their ability to work properly and they die. The adrenal glands also produce several hormones which are similar to those produced by the gonads. Overproduction of these hormones in women often results in excessive growth of hair on the face and lowering of the pitch of the individual's voice.

The *testes and ovaries* are primarily the sites of production of sperm and egg cells respectively—the union of which results in the beginning of a new life, a baby. They also produce hormones responsible for the physical development and characteristics of the male and female. During childhood these organs are not active but, when puberty begins, with stimulation by the pituitary hormones at this time, they start to produce the hormones peculiar to them. In the male they produce or help to produce the secondary sex characteristics: growth of beard, a deepening of the voice, muscle development, and the distribution of fat peculiar to him. In the female they produce secondary sex characteristics such as development of the mammary glands and the female fat distribution. In later life these organs contribute to the maintenance of these characteristics and the functional activity of the various parts of the genitalia. Loss of the gonads will result in cessation of germ cell production and, in the male, can cause a reversion to the female body characteristics with a redistribution of body fat and a change in the voice level.

In the female, the ovaries also control the menstrual period, the twenty-eight day non-pregnant cycle in which an egg is matured, shed (ovulated), and passed through the Fallopian tube into the uterus. The cycle ends with the beginning of bleeding, as the surface of the uterus, prepared for the fertilized egg, is shed. This is a complicated control system, and it is carried out with the aid of the pituitary gland. Together, they maintain a hormone balance that gradually shifts from one end of the cycle to the other. Thus, at the beginning of the cycle, all the effort is directed toward preparation of the uterus for the fertilized egg and the maturation of the egg while, toward the end of the cycle, no fertilization having taken place, the effort is directed toward the return of the uterus to its original state and preparation for the next cycle.

An Introduction to
HEALTH AND NUTRITION

The most precious gift anyone can ask for is good health. Without it there is neither peace of mind, ambition, nor security. Good nutrition is an insurance policy to good health. All systems and tissues in the body depend for their maintenance and existence on proper nourishment. This nourishment is obtained from the foods we eat and drink. Spectacular advances have been made in medicine in the last twenty-five years. Antibiotics have eliminated the danger from many infections, sparing thousands of lives every day. Newer knowledge of nutrition has saved untold numbers of people from dying of malnutrition and kindred diseases.

Prehistoric man combed the fields for roots and berries, the woods for animals, the waters for fish, and the skies for birds—collecting food to appease his hunger and maintain his health. Since the beginning of history, man has been searching for food, for ways to produce and process it, as well as to make it both palatable and nourishing.

Galen, a Greek scientist, (130-200 A.D.) experimented on domestic animals and found that the stomach was an organ of digestion which absorbed small particles of food. This was the beginning of the science of nutrition. Research in the field of nutrition continued at a slow pace until the beginning of the nineteenth century. Since then each span of fifty years has brought with it new advances in the scientific approach to better nutrition.

The twentieth century opened up a wide horizon for the application of this research to health and diseases. Chemists and physiologists worked to show the need of protein for better growth in man and animal. Then others set about to prove the necessity for minerals and vitamins as elements essential for a healthy body. As times changed, the need for research into other aspects of nutrition and metabolic spheres developed. Biochemistry, that branch of chemistry which deals with the chemical components and processes occurring in plants and animals, became an established science. The biochemist brought forth new components made up of a number of related substances formed as end products of protein digestion. Amino acids are the chief components of protein and some thirty have been isolated. Hormones, which are chemical substances secreted into the body fluids by certain endocrine or "ductless" glands, are another. They are transported by the fluids and produce a specific effect upon the activity of cells remote from their source. Enzymes are a third. These are complex organic substances which accelerate certain chemical transformations in plants and animals such as the digestion of food. They are present in the digestive juices. Research continues to isolate chemical regulators which aid man's nutrition.

From our nutrition we maintain life, and from good nutrition we maintain good health. However, it is not enough that a person has access to plenty of food. The food must be properly prepared and ingested before the body can utilize it. Sickness or disease very often causes an abstinence from food, which in turn may lead to malnutrition.

Chapter Eleven

NUTRIENTS

Certain nutrients are essential to maintain health. These are oxygen, water, proteins, carbohydrates, fats, and minerals. Without oxygen and water we could not survive. Without some of the amino acids in proteins, we could not live. Carbohydrates and fats are necessary for energy, growth, and emotional stability.

OXYGEN: Oxygen is an element which is indispensable to life. We get it from the air we breathe and the water we drink. It is the cheapest of all foods since it costs nothing. Shut off the supply of oxygen to the body and death will ensue within one or two minutes.

Oxygen is inhaled from the air into the lungs and passes through certain air spaces into the blood. It is then transported in chemical combination by the red corpuscles (these corpuscles act like little freight cars) to the cells of the body where it is then utilized as the main activator of cellular metabolism (similar to a match or flame which lights the fuel that is used to start a furnace or a locomotive).

Oxygen also has a relationship to the breathing mechanism of the body. In this connection its value lies in the formation of carbon dioxide which is the chemical composition that stimulates the respiratory center in the brain to produce what is known in animals and man as respiration or breathing.

There are certain conditions which exist where a person may have an insufficient amount of oxygen supplied to the cells of his body. These are found in certain types of heart, lung, and blood diseases. In most of these conditions oxygen must be made available in greater concentrations than that supplied in the normal air.

WATER: Water is composed of two parts hydrogen and one part oxygen. Its chemical formula is H_2O. Since we could not survive more than a few days without it, water becomes a very necessary element of food.

Water in any quantity can be taken with the meals, or between meals, without having any effect on the digestion. However, water has an effect on the body processes.

The body needs six to eight pints of liquid a day to maintain good nutrition. The reason for this is to regulate the body temperature by its evaporation through the skin. It also acts as a vehicle to eliminate waste material within the body through the urine and feces. The liquid aids the digestion by diluting digestive acids and foods in the stomach and intestines. It is the main body vehicle for blood and lymph and, without it, there would be no circulation of blood. This does not mean that we have to drink eight pints of water a day. Solid foods, such as meats, fish, vegetables, and fruits contain from 20 to 90 percent water. Vegetables such as asparagus, cucumbers, cabbage, cauliflower, eggplant, lettuce, tomatoes, and radishes are made up of 90 percent water. Fruits like melons, strawberries, and raspberries contain 90 percent water. There are many fruits which have 50 to 80 percent water. Beverages such as coffee, tea, milk, and buttermilk supply large quantities of water. In a twenty-four hour period the normal healthy individual usually excretes as much liquid as he takes in. This assures him a normal water balance.

PROTEINS: To survive one must have proteins. Foods which are high in protein contain certain chemicals without which we cannot live. These chemicals are called *amino acids,* and ten of them are indispensable. There are others which are sometimes known as "incomplete" proteins. Since these amino acids are found in varying amounts and in various forms in foods, in order to get the vital ones we must include all kinds of high protein foods in the diet. The best sources are milk and the white of eggs. Protein furnishes the elements for growth and repair of the body tissues in infants and children. It manufactures immune bodies which help resist infections. In the adult the need to continue the process of repair is necessary for health. An adequate daily intake of protein for an adult is one gram per kilogram (2.2 lbs.).

Foods which are high in protein are: milk and milk products such as dry skim milk, milk, buttermilk, evaporated milk, condensed milk, and cheese (butter is an exception, since it is not rich in protein), eggs, liver, kidney, all meats, poultry, fish, soybeans, nuts, peanut butter, dried beans, dried lentils, dried peas, and whole grain flour or cereals.

To get the daily protein requirements, every child or adult should have one pint to one quart of milk, one egg, one or two servings of meat, fish, cheese, whole grain bread or cereal.

CARBOHYDRATES: Carbohydrates are predominantly starches or sugar. They provide energy and heat. If an excess of carbohydrate is contained in the diet, it is converted into and stored in the body as fat. Foods high in carbohydrates are sugar, candy, chocolate, honey, syrups, jellies, preserves, jam, all kinds of flour, spaghetti, macaroni, cereals, bread, rolls, matzos, cakes, pies, crackers, barley, rice, cornstarch, beans, peas, lentils, fruits, beer and sodas.

FATS: About 40 to 60 percent of the calories in the average diet today consists of fat. This is too high because there is no reason to believe that more than a small amount of fat is essential to good health. There are certain fatty acids found in fats which are necessary to maintain good nutrition. These can be obtained from vegetable oils used in cooking or in salads. Too much fat in the diet may increase fat deposits on the liver and spleen and impair their function. After digestion takes place fat is absorbed and transported to the liver. If it is not used up for energy it may store itself on the liver in layers and slow up the utilization action of the liver. A similar storage or coating of the spleen with layers of fat will hinder its physiological action. Since the body uses carbohydrates for its energy requirements, fat is usually stored in the tissues and adds to body weight. This may also add an extra burden on the heart. For example, if a man's normal weight should be 150 pounds, but in reality he weighs 200 pounds, that individual is carrying an extra load of fifty pounds. The heart in order to handle the extra fifty pound load must do a little extra pumping to send the blood around the body to feed and take care of the added fat tissue. If this added weight is carried over a long period of time the heart may enlarge in order to compensate for the extra workload put upon it.

Fats are found in both animal and vegetable foods. Foods high in fats are butter, margarine, animal fats, vegetable oils, pork products, liver, egg yolk, whole milk, cream, sour cream, ice cream, custard, cheeses, lamb, veal, fowl, and chocolate bars.

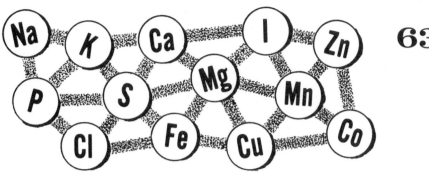

MINERALS: Minerals, some of which are called *trace* elements, are needed for good nutrition. They are sodium, potassium, chlorine, calcium, phosphorus, sulfur, magnesium, iron, copper, iodine, manganese, cobalt, zinc, fluorine and silicon. These are present in many foods.

The *sodium* ions are important to maintain the body fluids at a neutral reaction. A low sodium content lowers protein digestion. An increase of sodium, which is found in table salt, may result in an edema (increase of water in the tissues) which develops because of a disturbed water balance. In some conditions such as prolonged vomiting, diarrhea, or profuse perspiration there is usually a marked loss of sodium from the tissues which may produce weakness. This sodium may be replaced by use of extra amounts of salt, and in severe depletion it may become necessary to administer salt solution into the veins.

Potassium is present to a greater extent in the body than sodium. It is found mostly within the cells while sodium is found mostly in the extracellular fluid (outside the body cell). It has been demonstrated that potassium has an association with the function of the muscles and has a close balance with calcium in maintaining nerve irritability or excitement.

Chlorine is found in combination with sodium in the blood and exercises some influence on metabolism. It also aids in the regulation and stimulation of muscle action. Chlorine is also present in the acid juices of the stomach and aids digestion.

One percent of the body's *calcium* is found in the blood and soft tissues. It is the best constituent in the structure of the bones in a child's growth and development. Calcium, with the help of vitamin D, helps to form and maintain sound bone structure, and healthy teeth, finger nails, and toe nails. Calcium aids in the proper functioning of the nerves and muscles of the body including the heart muscles. If a deficiency of calcium exists then children and even adults may tend to be nervous, develop soft bone structure, cavities in their teeth, and poor growth of the nails on their fingers and toes.

The mineral *phosphorus* probably has more functions than any other. It is concerned with carbohydrate metabolism, protein metabolism, fat metabolism, normal muscle metabolism, brain and nerve metabolism, normal blood chemistry, and the development of tooth and bone growth. Phosphorus, together with calcium, is utilized in promoting bone formation.

Sulfur is an important mineral. It is part of some of the amino acids (proteins). It also is an ingredient of many vitamins. Excessive amounts may result in toxic reactions.

About 70% of the body's *magnesium* is present in the bones. Rarely does one see a magnesium deficiency.

Iron is one of the most vital elements in the body. It is part of the hemoglobin in the blood and is necessary for producing young cells (reticulocytes) to transport oxygen and carbon dioxide. The iron level in the body is regulated by the absorption of iron from the foods we eat.

Copper is closely associated with iron since it, too, is necessary for the formation of hemoglobin in the blood. A copper deficiency results in a poor utilization of iron in the liver, anemia and changes in bone and skin. It may also result in loss of calcium and phosphorus from the bones, making them susceptible to fractures. It aids a certain enzyme (a substance produced by plants and animals and found in the juices of digestion) to form pigment in the body.

Nearly all of the *iodine* of the body is located in the thyroid gland. Iodine deficiency leads to an increase in size of the thyroid gland and may result in a goitre. This seems to occur more frequently in areas away from the seacoast. Iodized salt is used to supply the body with this mineral.

Not too much is known about the element *manganese*. It is

thought to have some effect on growth and on producing a sufficient amount of milk in the mother of a newborn child. However, in some pregnant women an increased amount may cause abortions to occur.

Cobalt is a small part of vitamin B_{12} which acts as a preventive of pernicious anemia. It may also be used to stimulate the appetite where such stimulation is needed.

Zinc is usually associated with hair growth and has some influence on carbohydrate metabolism.

There are approximately 15 *vitamins*. These are substances which are necessary to life. They are essential for growth and health although they furnish neither heat, energy, nor material for building tissue. Small amounts are adequate, but the lack of even a small amount of one of them may result in some disease. Deficiencies are usually recognized. The body is not able to store vitamins for reserve as it does fats and carbohydrates. There is a close relationship between many vitamins, while others are completely separate and on their own.

The best sources of vitamins are found in the natural foods. A menu containing the basic four will furnish an adequate amount of vitamins and minerals to keep a person in good nutritional health. Foods should be prepared and cooked with a minimum loss of these elements by using heat which is not too high and by not using too much liquid. Many of the vitamins are in the liquid and this is very often discarded by the cook.

Because of the amount of advertising that is done about vitamins people may be under the impression that they do not have to worry about preparing food properly or even about the kinds of foods they serve their families. They may have the impression that if a commercially prepared vitamin and mineral pill or capsule is taken instead, it will supply all the necessary nutrition needed. This is a fallacy! You can get the best vitamins and minerals when they are found in their natural habitat such as foods. No synthetic preparation can compete with natural vitamins. There may be some indication to take commercially prepared vitamin or vitamin and mineral formulas when your doctor feels that a deficiency exists and he would like to supplement the diet with additional nutrients.

VITAMIN A: Vitamin A is an organic compound found only in animals such as birds, fish, and mammals. There are plant foods which contain carotene (yellow pigment). These carotinoid plant foods are precursors of vitamin A. Two forms have been identified, vitamin A-1 which is found in the livers of salt water fish; vitamin A-2 found in the livers of fresh water fish. Since they resemble each other physiologically we treat them as one and call them collectively vitamin A.

Vitamin A is measured in International Units (I.U.). The recommended allowance for adults is 5,000 I.U. a day and for infants 2,000 I.U. a day. In children a deficiency of this vitamin may manifest itself in retarded growth, impairment of the bones and teeth, and susceptibility to infection. In adults a deficiency may produce excessive dryness of the skin and night-blindness. Mineral oil used as a laxative or in salad dressings destroys vitamin A.

Absorption of vitamin A takes from three to five hours after food is ingested and 95% is stored in the liver. As with most fat soluble vitamins it is excreted through the bowels.

Excessive doses of vitamin A (over 50,000 units a day) may result in toxic symptoms in both children and adults. This may produce coarsening of the skin with an itching rash, thinning of the hair, pain in the joints, and hemorrhage between the bone and its covering.

VITAMIN B_1: Vitamin B_1, known as thiamine, is soluble in water. All foods with the exception of fats, oils, and refined sugars contain some thiamine. No food contains excessive amounts of this necessary vitamin.

Thiamine requirement is measured in milligrams. The dose depends on the total number of calories consumed in a day. Regardless of age, an allowance of 0.5 mgm. per 1,000 calories for intakes of less than 3,000 calories a day and 0.2 mgm. for each additional 1,000 calories in diet determines the thiamine need. Average daily dose for infants is 0.5 mgm. and adults 1.5 mgm.

A deficiency of this vitamin may cause loss of appetite, constipation, and tenderness of the calf muscles of the legs. Polyneuritis or an inflammation of many nerves may result as a lack of this vitamin. Persons on a diet rich in carbohydrates (sugars and starches) show symptoms of thiamine deficiency. In excessive alcoholism there is usually an associated vitamin B_1 deficiency. Also fatigue, weariness, labored breathing, nausea, depression, changes in the electrocardiogram, low excretion of thiamine in the urine and an increase in pyruvic acid in the blood occur. Some of these symptoms may also occur in a deficiency of other nutrients.

VITAMIN B$_2$: Vitamin B$_2$ or riboflavin is found in all plant and animal foods. This vitamin, which is soluble in water, is also known as vitamin G, flavin, lactoflavin, and riboflavin. It is essential for growth and is involved in the metabolism of energy nutrients. A deficiency of this vitamin may cause a deficiency of other vitamins in the B complex (vitamin B$_1$ and niacin). Riboflavin deficiency is manifested by cracks or sores at the corners of the lips or mouth, conjunctivitis, and watering of the eyes. Normal daily requirement for infants is 0.5 mgm. and for adults 1.5 mgm.

VITAMIN B$_6$: Vitamin B$_6$ or pyridoxine is dependent on several enzyme systems that help in the metabolism of proteins, amino acids, and fatty acids, especially the unsaturated fats. It also aids in the formation of new amino acids and in the conversion of tryptophan to the vitamin niacin.

Vitamin B$_6$ exists in almost all foods and for this reason a deficiency seldom exists. However, where a deficiency of this vitamin is present it sometimes causes nausea and vomiting of pregnancy, convulsions, anemia, weakness, nervousness, insomnia, radiation sickness from x-rays, and difficulty in walking.

No daily minimum requirements have been established.

VITAMIN B$_{12}$: In the stomach juices there is an intrinsic factor present. When a lack of this substance exists and B$_{12}$ becomes unavailable it results in pernicious anemia. The average diet of meat, eggs, and milk more than takes care of the needs for vitamin B$_{12}$.

VITAMIN C: Vitamin C or ascorbic acid is a water soluble vitamin and like calcium it is most often low in the diet of all ages. It has assumed an important place in medicine because it is like a binding which holds the cells in proper relation to each other and to the fluid which bathes and nourishes them. Another function of this vitamin is that of increasing the resistance to infection.

A deficiency of vitamin C produces a weakening of the walls of the capillaries (tiny blood vessels) resulting in hemorrhages of varying degrees, retardation of growth because of its effect on bones and cartilages, irritability, changes in the gums and teeth.

Scurvy is a leading disease resulting from a deficiency of vitamin C. The signs and symptoms of scurvy are as follows: inflammation of the gums (gingivitis), infection, loosening of the teeth, tenderness of the legs, anemia, spider-like hemorrhages under the skin, and black and blue marks without any apparent cause. In severe deficiency one may suffer from bleeding from the stomach or intestines.

Scurvy in infants is manifested by pain, tenderness, swelling of the thighs and legs, paleness, and crying of the baby when it is picked up and handled.

The daily requirement in children 75mg., adults 70 mg., pregnant women 100 mg., nursing mothers 150 mg.

VITAMIN D: Vitamin D is a fat soluble vitamin that is necessary for the formation of normal bone tissue and for the calcification of bones which have rickets. In an infant, rickets usually develops at the age of six months. In a premature infant rickets may be more severe because the fetus obtains about 85% of its stored calcium during the last three months of the pregnancy. Therefore, if it is born earlier it may not have its full body supply of needed calcium. Large doses of vitamin D are essential to remedy such a condition.

Vitamin D deficiency in older children or adults may result from a lack of sunshine or from omitting foods from the diet which are high in vitamin D. A low amount of calcium in the blood may produce poor teeth.

Vitamin D also increases the absorption of calcium from the intestines.

A deficiency of vitamin D and calcium in the diet of adults may result in osteomalacia (softening of the bones).

Large doses of vitamin D, if taken over a long period of time, may produce toxic effects. They may develop loss of appetite, thirst, nausea, vomiting, diarrhea, headache, drowsiness, as well as loss of weight.

The recommended daily allowance is 400 I.U. (International Units) for children and adults alike.

VITAMIN E: Vitamin E is a fat soluble and is stored in the body tissues. This vitamin contains an active substance known as alpha-tocopherol. It is a controversial vitamin because it was postulated that a deficiency of it was responsible for the cause of sterility in the male rat and led to abortion or miscarriage, though not a failure to conceive, in the female rat. This has not been demonstrated at all times on humans. Vitamin E is being used in the treatment of muscular dystrophy with some encouraging results.

It is found in nearly all types of foods but to a greater degree in wheat germ oil and the germ of most cereal seeds, also in corn oil and cotton seed oil. Considerable tocopherol is present in milk, butter, eggs and liver. An impression has been created that vitamin E in large doses would prevent many different types of heart disease. This has not been shown to be true.

People whose diet includes fruit, vegetables, milk, whole grain cereals, meat, and eggs every day will not have to be concerned about having a deficiency of vitamin E.

VITAMIN K: Vitamin K is a fat soluble vitamin and its existence in the body is important when there is a deficiency of prothrombin which is necessary for normal blood clotting. If a deficiency of vitamin K exists then prolonged and serious hemorrhages may take place.

During prolonged antibiotic therapy, bleeding and hemorrhage may occur because vitamin K may be diminished by the action of some bacteria. The body usually has an adequate supply of vitamin K for its needs.

FOLIC ACID: This vitamin is useful in the treatment of many anemias particularly pernicious anemia of pregnancy, also liver disorders, and digestive disturbances.

NIACIN: This vitamin is soluble in water and is known as the antipellagra vitamin because it prevents this disease from occurring when the diet is adequate in this vitamin. Persons on a diet deficient in niacin develop a skin rash, diarrhea, insomnia, and emotional instability.

A urine analysis will show a deficiency of a dietary intake of niacin or tryptophan containing proteins.

If dietary levels of less than 7.5 mg. a day exist then pellagra may manifest itself. This disease is prevalent where corn is the main constituent of the daily diet.

The minimum daily requirements are, infants 5 mg., adults 10 mg.

PANTOTHENIC ACID: A number of years ago, pantothenic acid was considered as a vitamin that had the ability to restore greying hair to its natural color. The value of the vitamin for this purpose was demonstrated in the rat but it did not prove to be as successful in the case of man.

There is some doubt that a deficiency of this vitamin actually occurs except under unusual circumstances. However, if a deficiency of pantothenic acid should exist it may produce a numbness or burning sensation in the hands and feet with signs of muscular weakness, as well.

SOURCES OF VITAMINS IN FOOD

VITAMIN A
Good sources of vitamin A are:

Liver, carrots, sweet potatoes, spinach, yellow peaches, yellow corn, butter, margarine, greens, apricots, tomatoes, peas, broccoli, cantaloupe.

(In addition to green and yellow vegetables, whole milk and yellow cheese are sources of vitamin A.)

THIAMINE
Good sources of thiamine are:

Kidney, heart, pork (lean), liver, peas (green and dried), soybeans, lamb, bread (enriched and whole wheat), cereal (enriched whole grain and fortified), oysters, watermelon, potatoes, milk.

(In addition, green leafy vegetables are sources of thiamine.)

NIACIN
Good sources of niacin are:

Liver, chicken, lamb, salmon, tuna fish, peanut butter, bread (enriched and whole wheat), peas (fresh green), brown rice.

(In addition, other lean meat, poultry, canned fish and enriched cereal products are sources of niacin.)

RIBOFLAVIN
Good sources of riboflavin are:
>Liver, heart, milk, meat (lean), greens, eggs, chicken, beans (dried), oysters, fish, lima beans.

(Also tongue, enriched bread, turkey, cheddar cheese and salmon are sources of riboflavin.)

VITAMIN C
Good sources of vitamin C are:
>Oranges, grapefruit, tomatoes, greens, strawberries, potatoes, cabbage, green pepper, pineapple, sweet potato.

(In addition, other berries and cantaloupe are sources of vitamin C. The foods should be fresh and prepared just before serving. Eat vitamin C foods raw when possible.)

VITAMIN D
Good sources of vitamin D are:
>Foods fortified with vitamin D, fish liver oils, vitamin D concentrates. (Sun shining directly on the skin helps the body make its own vitamin D.)

PROTEIN
Good sources of animal and vegetable protein are:
>Meat (lean), fish, poultry, eggs, milk, cheese, peas (dried), beans (dried), soybeans, nuts, bread (enriched and whole wheat), cereals (whole grain and enriched).

(Eat some animal protein each day.)

CALCIUM
Good sources of calcium are:

Milk, kale, collards, cheese (yellow), mustard greens, turnip greens, ice cream, oysters, shrimp, canned salmon, broccoli, dried figs, clams, egg yolk.

(In addition, dried beans, nuts, self-rising flour and enriched self-rising flour supply some calcium.)

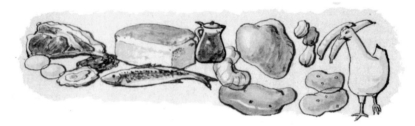

IRON
Good sources of iron are:

Liver, meat (lean), eggs, oysters, greens, molasses and sorghum, dried fruits, beans, fowl, potatoes, fish, enriched bread, enriched cereals.

(In addition, heart, kidney, whole grain and enriched cereals are good sources of iron.)

IODINE
Good sources of iodine are:

Iodized salt, sea food (salt water fish), green vegetables, milk and water in areas where soil contains iodine.

Chapter Twelve

DIET

In discussing diets for maintaining good health, there are certain facts which we must know.

Attention should be given to elimination of waste material regularly. The bowel habit depends, in a great measure, on the quantity and quality of foods one eats. Some people may be considered normal if they have a movement once or twice a day. In others it may be normal if they eliminate once or twice a week. Many people are too busy to go to the toilet. This sets up a reaction of constipation which results in distention of the large bowel. In some people this is not serious, but rather a common occurrence. In others it may produce a feeling of lethargy and cramps in the abdomen. It is a fallacy to assume that large quantities of food are necessary for healthy elimination. Food in abundance taxes not only the digestive system but puts a load on the heart as well. It is better to eat to live than to live to eat.

Geographical locations, climatic conditions, cultural environment, emotional ties, and religious training often govern what one eats. An Eskimo could hardly survive on fruits and plants from the tropics. A person living in the tropics of Java could scarcely be comfortable on the high fat diet which one finds in Greenland. An individual traveling from the temperate zone to the torrid or frigid zones finds that digestive disturbances frequently occur. In a tropical country one must be on a diet that will facilitate the loss of body heat; while in a frigid climate one must eat the foodstuffs that will harness body heat. With regard to nutrition, each geographic group must be considered in the light of its own environment. For centuries man has been accustomed either to a vegetarian regime such as that of the inhabitants of the tropics, or a high meat and fat diet as exemplified by the foods eaten by the people of the Arctic. For our purposes, a blending of vegetables and meats seems to give the best results.

We must also consider that the direction of a diet depends upon habits and the emotional and physical health of an individual. In times of emotional stress, one may overeat or undereat. Behavior patterns and environment also are factors in determining the amount of food consumed. (This is explained in more detail in the chapter on Obesity.)

TIME REQUIRED FOR FOOD TO PASS THROUGH THE STOMACH

The following table indicates the length of time food remains in the stomach. It will be observed that foods rich in fats or proteins require much longer digestion time than foods which are rich in sugars or starches.

The inside lining of the stomach contains thousands of tiny glands that manufacture a juice to aid digestion. This is known as the gastric juice. It is made up of hydrochloric acid and pepsin which is an enzyme. Fats and carbohydrates pass through the stomach without any alterations, but the gastric juice helps in the digestion of protein foods.

Most foods are passed through the stomach and into the small intestine in a matter of two to six hours. The composition of the foods and the activity of the small intestines are the factors responsible for the rate of speed which sends the foods through the stomach. Fat is usually delayed in the stomach in order to keep the stomach from pushing more fat into the small intestine than it can physiologically hold. If too much fat accumulates in the small intestine a hormone enters at this point and slows down the gastric juice and the movements of the stomach. After fat passes through the small intestine the hormone diminishes and the stomach then resumes its normal amount of gastric juice and its normal activity.

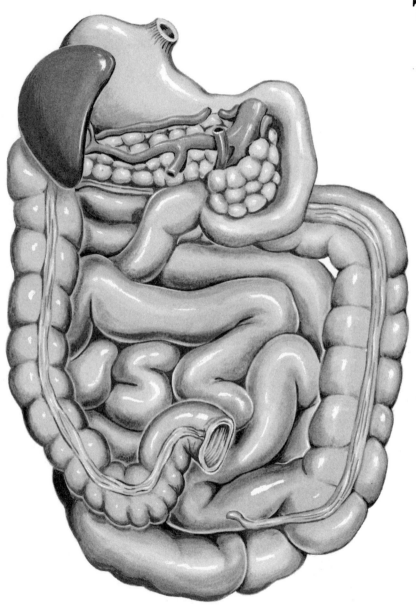

LOWER DIGESTIVE TRACT

DIGESTIBILITY OF FOODS*

FOOD	PORTION		HOURS	MINUTES
Fruits	1	Portion	2	20
Vegetables, Cooked	2	Tablespoons	2	15
Milk	1	Glass	2	30
Bread	1	Slice	2	40
Cereals	1	Portion	2	40
Pie	1	Portion	2	30
Cakes	1	Small Piece	3	
Puddings	1	Portion	2	20
Sugar and Candies	1	Piece	2	05
Ices	1	Dip	2	35
Ice Cream	1	Dip	3	15
Eggs, Soft Boiled	2		1	45
Eggs, Raw	2		2	15
Eggs, Poached	2		2	30
Eggs, Hard Boiled	2		3	
Egg Omelet	2		3	
Fish, Baked	1	Portion	2	50
Fish, Fried	1	Portion	3	15
Steak	¼	Pound	4	
Roast Beef	¼	Pound	4	
Roast Veal	¼	Pound	4	15
Ham, Boiled	¼	Pound	3	30
Roast Pork	¼	Pound	4	
Pork Chops, Broiled	1	Chop	2	45
Pork Chops, Fried	1	Chop	5	
Lamb, Roast	¼	Pound	3	45
Lamb Chops, Broiled	1	Chop	2	35
Lamb Chops, Fried	1	Chop	5	
Chicken, Boiled	¼	Pound	2	45
Chicken, Roast	¼	Pound	4	15
Chicken, Fried	¼	Pound	5	
Turkey, Roast	¼	Pound	4	
Duck, Roast	¼	Pound	5	
Tongue, Smoked	¼	Pound	4	15
Frankfurter	1	Frank	3	45
Bologna	¼	Pound	4	
Salami	¼	Pound	5	

A double portion of any food will require twice the amount of time to pass through the stomach.

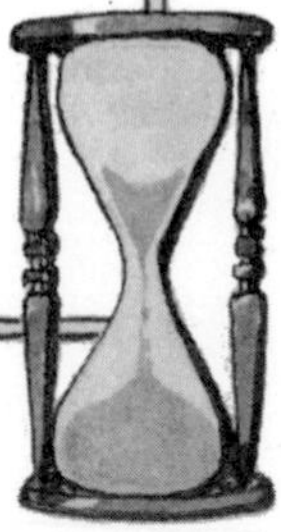

THE BASIC FOUR GROUPS

There is no such thing as the "ideal" food. Some foods furnish more than one nutrient, but all of those listed in the basic four groups are essential for adequate nutrition. They provide the proteins, carbohydrates, fats, vitamins and minerals necessary to maintain good health. It is suggested that housewives should plan their daily menus around these four important groups. These are dairy foods, meat group, vegetables and fruits, breads and cereals. They are essential for everyone — children, teenagers, and adults. The menu plan shows one way to include the basic four groups in a day's meal.

A DAILY FOOD GUIDE*

DAIRY FOODS: Milk, use daily. 3 to 4 glasses—children; 4 or more—teenagers; 2 or more glasses —adults; 4 or more glasses—pregnant women; 6 or more glasses—nursing mothers. (A glass—8 oz. or ¼ qt. of milk).

These quantities of milk provide about ⅔ of the day's calcium recommended for good nutrition. Cheese, ice cream and other milk-made foods can supply part of the milk. Use milk as a beverage and in cooking – in hot cereals, milk soups, white sauces, puddings and custards. Pour on fruit, cereal and puddings. The combination of milk with cereal or bread is excellent, especially in meals where little or no meat or eggs is served. The proteins in milk make those in cereals and bread more useful in the body. Milk is our main source of calcium in foods. For calcium: 1 slice American cheese (1 oz.) = ⅔ glass milk, ½ cup creamed cottage cheese = ⅓ glass milk, ½ cup (¼ pt.) ice cream = ¼ glass milk. Milk also contributes fine quality protein, vitamins . . . especially riboflavin and vitamin A – and many other nutrients. For children, 4 glasses of milk supply about ½ the protein recommended daily and over ½ the riboflavin. For adults, 2 glasses of milk supply about ¼ the protein and nearly ½ the riboflavin. Skim milk lacks the fat of whole milk and its vitamin A (unless fortified); other food values are the same as in whole milk. Butter supplies milk's flavorful and easily digested fat along with its vitamin A. One glass of skim milk plus 1 scant tablespoon of butter equals the food value of whole milk.

MEAT GROUP: (Use 2 or more servings daily.) Meat, fish, poultry, eggs, or cheese—with dry beans, peas, nuts or peanut butter as alternates.

Use amounts of these foods to supply at least as much protein as that in 4 ounces of cooked lean meat (about ⅓ pound raw). Teenagers, pregnant women and nursing mothers need larger amounts of these foods. Good practices to follow are: An egg a day or at least 3 to 5 a week. Liver, heart, kidney, or sweetbread about once a week. Other kinds of meat, fish, poultry or cheese, 4 to 5 or more times a week. With dried beans, peas, nuts or peanut butter, serve milk or cheese. The animal protein makes the vegetable protein more useful in the body. Foods in the meat group are counted on to supply about ½ the protein recommended daily for good nutrition. Two servings for an adult might be, for example . . . 1 medium serving meat (3 ounces, cooked) plus 1 egg. Choose combinations from the following which are about equal in amount of protein:

    1 oz. cooked lean meat, poultry, or fish
    1 egg
    1 slice cheese, American or Swiss (1 oz.)
    2 tablespoons creamed cottage cheese (1 oz.)
    2 tablespoons peanut butter (1 oz.)
    ½ cup cooked dried beans or peas

Eggs and meat, especially liver, are important for iron; also for B-vitamins. Pork supplies large amounts of the B-vitamin, thiamine. The legumes — dried beans, peas, nuts — are good sources of iron and thiamine, but their protein should be supplemented with an animal protein.

VEGETABLES & FRUITS: Use 4 or more servings daily. Include a dark green leafy or deep yellow vegetable or yellow fruit at least 3 or 4 times a week for vitamin A; a citrus fruit, or tomatoes, or other good source of vitamin C every day.

Use other vegetables and fruits for variety as well as their minerals, vitamins, and roughage. Use potatoes frequently for all these food values plus food energy. Use fresh, canned or frozen vegetables and fruits. Save food values and flavors of vegetables by cooking quickly in small amounts of water. Dried fruits are valuable for iron. A serving is ½ cup or more. Foods in this group should supply over half the vitamin A and all of the vitamin C recommended daily for good nutrition. Vegetables and fruits high in vitamin A are: broccoli, chard, all "greens," kale, spinach, carrots, sweet potatoes, tomatoes, cantaloupe, apricots. These are about equal in vitamin C: 1 medium orange, ¾ cup juice, ½ grapefruit, ¾ cup juice, 2 medium tomatoes, 2 cups juice, ½ large cantaloupe, 1 cup strawberries, ¾ cup broccoli, 1½ cups cabbage, raw, shredded.

BREADS & CEREALS: Use 4 or more servings daily. Use enriched or whole grain products. Check labels!

Choose from breads, cooked and ready-to-eat cereals, cornmeal, crackers, grits, spaghetti and macaroni, noodles, rice, quick breads and other baked goods if made with whole-grain or enriched flour. A serving is 1 slice of bread; ½ to ¾ cup of cereal. Foods in this group supply valuable amounts of protein, iron, several B-vitamins, and food energy. Cereals cooked and/or served with milk and breads made with milk are improved in quality of protein as well as quantity of protein, minerals, and vitamins. ADDITIONAL FOODS: The foods recommended form the foundation for a good diet. In general, use smaller servings for young children, except in milk; teenagers, pregnant and nursing mothers need more or larger servings. Most nutrient needs are met by the amounts of foods suggested by the "Guide" but more food for energy, or calories, is usually required according to individual age, size, and activity. More calories are consumed when foods are prepared or eaten with added butter, other fats or oils, sugars or syrups.

Meeting energy needs with more foods chosen from these four food groups will help to achieve an adequate diet. Calorie restricted diets can be more pleasing and satisfying when energy comes mostly from foods in these four groups. Some source of vitamin D should be included for infants and children, expectant and nursing mothers, and adults getting little sunshine. Good sources are vitamin D milk, fish liver oils, and direct sunshine.

Courtesy of National Dairy Council (2nd Ed. © 1958)

80 MENU PLAN

A daily food guide helps you plan or choose pleasing and satisfying meals that provide good nutrition. It suggests minimum amounts of food from each of 4 food groups which should be included in each day's meals. This menu plan shows one way to include the 4 important food groups in a day's meals. Vary your menus to suit your taste.

BREAKFAST	LUNCH	DINNER
Fruit	Main Protein Dish	Main Protein Dish
Cereal or Egg or both	Vegetable	Vegetable — Potato
Toast or Roll & Butter	Bread & Butter	Bread or Roll & Butter
Milk — Coffee	Milk — Fruit	Milk — Dessert

LIQUID DIETS

Physicians prescribe liquid diets for patients for many and diverse reasons. Some of them are as follows: — (1) in patients where partial or total removal of the stomach was done surgically for an ulcer or cancer of the stomach; (2) in patients when a clot forms in the cerebral (brain) arteries, paralysis of the tongue and pharynx results making it impossible to take food by mouth since the swallowing mechanism is gone; liquid diets are fed through a tube which is inserted in the nose, down through the esophagus and into the stomach; (3) in psychiatric patients who refuse to eat, forced feedings with a liquid diet by tube is the route of choice; (4) in fractures of the jaw bones feeding through a straw is the usual procedure.

In persons who have none of the above disabilities and are in good health liquid diets are not desirable. There are many formula diets on the market today that are being recommended for weight reduction. These preparations were originally manufactured as a multi-purpose food to be used as a supplement to the diets of people who live in depressed areas of the world. Since their normal diets are poor in nutrients, a multi-purpose formula was advocated to enhance their nutritional status. In this country where food is so plentiful and where every conceivable type of nutritious food is available, there is no need for fad diets. Whether a person needs 900 calories or 1500 calories a day, there is no reason to drink a food when you can chew and eat it which is more suitable to our way of life. Meat, fish, eggs, cereal, cooked vegetables or a green vegetable salad has more eye appeal and tastes lots better than a formula drink as a steady diet. When one goes on any liquid diet or any diet that has "one-ness," it is considered a fad diet and carries with it the penalties of fad dieting. Persons who are not on a controlled therapeutic liquid regime run the risk of developing gall stones and sometimes kidney stones because the fats from the body are mobilized into the blood stream too rapidly and jam up in the gall bladder forming stones.

A liquid preparation such as a glass of milk, buttermilk, malted milk, soup, or a liquid formula may be all right as a substitute for one meal a day provided the other two meals are nutritionally adequate. Good eating habits should be established by every person who wants to have continued good health and prepare his or her body for the processes of aging which one day will be so important to all.

SUGGESTED DIETS IN PREGNANCY AND LACTATION

GENERAL RULES:

1. The foods in chart form are those which are needed to meet basic requirements for protein, minerals and vitamins. *Caloric intake should be set by the physician since it is an individual matter.*

2. Calcium tablets are not a complete substitute for milk because they do not supply the protein or vitamins found in milk.

3. Foods which may cause discomfort or are excessive in calories and should be avoided are:

> Beverages — Large amounts of tea and coffee, wine or other alcoholic drinks, soft drinks

> Desserts — Foods rich in starch, sugar and fat such as rich pastries, cakes, puddings and ice cream

> Meat, Fish and Poultry — Fatty meats and gravies

> Miscellaneous — Fried foods, mayonnaise, highly seasoned foods, large amounts of salt and nuts

> Potato and Substitute — Macaroni, spaghetti and potato chips

> Sweets — Candy, sugar, jam, jelly and marmalade

> Vegetables — Broccoli, Brussels sprouts, cabbage, cauliflower, corn, lima beans, onions, turnips

4. If the recommended diet is followed, it will not be necessary to use vitamin or mineral preparations unless they have been ordered by the physician.

	FIRST & SECOND TRIMESTER	THIRD TRIMESTER	LACTATION
BEVERAGES	All — include at least 4 cups milk.*	All — include at least 4 cups milk.*	All — include at least 6 cups milk.*
BREAD AND CEREALS	All — include ½ cup cereal and at least 2 slices bread.	All — include ½ cup cereal and at least 2 slices bread.	All — include at least ½ cup cereal and at least 2 slices bread.
CHEESE	All	All	All
DESSERTS	See Rule 3.	See Rule 3.	See Rule 3.
EGGS	3-5 weekly	1 daily	1 daily
FATS	Include 6 teaspoons butter or margarine.	Include 8 teaspoons butter or margarine.	Include 10 teaspoons butter or margarine.
FRUITS	Include 3 servings (½ cup each) daily one of which is citrus.	Include 3 servings (½ cup each) daily two of which are citrus.	Include 4 servings (½ cup each) daily two of which are citrus.
MEAT, FISH, POULTRY OR EQUIVALENTS	Include 4 ounces daily. Liver should be used once a week.	Include 7 ounces daily. Liver should be used once a week.	Include 7 ounces daily. Liver should be used once a week.
MISCELLANEOUS	See Rule 3.	See Rule 3.	See Rule 3.
POTATO AND SUBSTITUTES	Include 1 potato daily.	Include 1 potato daily.	Include 1 potato daily.
SOUPS	Clear broths; cream soups made from milk allowance.	Clear broths; cream soup made from milk allowance.	Clear broths; cream soup made from milk allowance.
SWEETS	See Rule 3.	See Rule 3.	See Rule 3.
VEGETABLES	Include 4 servings (½ cup each). Include 1 dark green, 1 yellow and 1 raw.	Include 4 servings (½ cup each). Include 1 dark green, 1 yellow and 1 raw.	Include 4 servings (½ cup each). Include 1 dark green, 1 yellow and 1 raw.

*One ounce of cheddar type cheese may be substituted for one cup of milk.

Chapter Thirteen

OBESITY AND UNDERWEIGHT

Obesity is the deposit of fat in excessive amounts in the body. There are many reasons why this occurs. The most common is that more calories are ingested than are used up in energy.

Most people like to blame their increased weight on "glandular trouble," "heredity," and "waste retention." These factors account for only 4 or 5% of all overweight or obese persons. The other 95% are obese because they take in more calories than they use. A person is considered obese if he weighs more than 10% above the theoretical normal for his height.

Obesity and overweight are terms used synonymously to describe a person who is heavier than he should be according to desirable standards. Actually, there is a difference between the two terms. A person is overweight when he has an increased amount of muscle tissue which may or may not be covered with fat, while a person is considered obese when he has a normal amount of muscle tissue but an excessive amount of fat.

HAZARDS OF OVERWEIGHT:

Statistics show that the death rate of moderately obese persons is 42%, and, in the markedly obese, it is 79% for men and 61% for women (Metropolitan Life Insurance Company).

In my own series of eight thousand obese patients I found that 72% have some degree of anemia, 37% nervousness or psychic disturbances, 22% heart or blood vessel diseases, 18% diabetes and 7% gall bladder diseases. Obese people with high blood pressure invariably get a substantial reduction in the blood pressure when they reduce their weight. The benefits from such a regimen reduce the chances of developing heart failure, kidney disorder, or a stroke. Obesity is responsible for preventing conception and causing many obstetrical complications.

A person who is obese is a good candidate for infections, particularly pneumonia. Many surgeons will refuse to operate on an obese person until a weight loss is accomplished. This is done to reduce the risk of surgical complications.

FAMILIAL OBESITY:

In families where certain articles of food have been served since childhood one grows up with a desire for these foods. This is particularly true among races where certain dietary habits are characteristic. It is difficult to determine in a man which is responsible for his obesity — heredity or environment. We know that whichever it is, overeating and inactivity exist, and these must assume the blame for the increase in weight. There are many families in which several members are obese. In these families, food assumes an important place in their family life. When an infant cries, a piece of zwieback, a cookie, bread or a pacifier is put into his mouth. The baby soons learns to expect something to eat anytime he suffers discomfort. As he grows to childhood, eating habits are established by his parents. A lollipop, pretzel, soda, chocolate bar, or ice cream on a stick become bargaining agents to keep him quiet. Rather than let "junior" cry, it is easier to keep his mouth occupied and thus keep him quiet. Now frustrations begin! Most of us are frustrated for one reason or another.

There are some persons who have a small waistline but have large thighs or large arms. When they are examined or x-rayed it is often observed that they have little or no fat covering these muscles but they do have abnormal increase in muscle tissue. This is an hereditary factor and no amount of dieting will help to reduce these areas, because one does not lose muscle by dieting, he only loses fat.

Studies of hereditary factors show that the offspring of obese parents are twice as variable in excessive body build as in slender build. Obese individuals may carry at least three genetic factors influencing obesity. They may carry genes for slenderness as well; hence we may find a lean member in a family of excessive obesity. Lean people very rarely carry genes for obesity. Variations in body build, such as a normal body with very heavy thighs, may come from the genes of one parent.

In the author's series of eight thousand obese patients, 72% had at least one obese parent, while in 23% both parents were obese. On the face of such high percentages favoring hereditary factors, one must take into consideration environmental eating habits. Certain types of diets are predominant in various racial and religious groups. The Italians favor abundance of starches, oils, spices. The Jewish people like to supplement their diet with fatty foods, sweets, and fruits. The Poles enjoy pork products and sweets. And so it is with various groups that are prone to influences of climate and national origin. One investigator showed the variability of progeny from different matings as follows:

	OBESE	NON OBESE
2 stout parents in 65 families produced	78%	27%
1 stout and 1 non-stout in 70 families produced	41.2%	58.8%
2 non-stout parents in 16 families produced	9.1%	90.9%

The question remains as to whether there are independent genes for obesity and leanness which are transmitted alone, or whether they exist in conjunction with genes of the nervous system or some other genetic independent causative factors. Heredity and environment are more often than not intertwined and have an influence on each other.

EMOTIONAL FACTORS:

Emotional problems are quite common in obese individuals. Such disorders may cause not only neuroses, but many sorts of behaviour problems that result in self inflicted misery. These may also occur when a person goes on a very strict or fad dietary regime. Anxieties, frustrations, nervousness, dizziness, weakness and depression are common complaints. These obese individuals do not wish to "grow up." They do not want to assume the responsibility and independence of adulthood. On the other hand, some turn to food as a "crutch" to fill a void due to a lack of affection and attention from parents. This is particularly true in children where both parents are working or in families that are separated or divorced. The young child or teenager misses the normal family relationship. Frustrated demands for love and affection may make unconscious nibblers. The outlet of this urge in children or adults creates a demand for more food, thereby leading to obesity. A bad or hectic day at the office, sickness, or death in a family may produce enough trauma for one to use food as a pacifier.

HUNGER AND APPETITE:

Hunger is an unpleasant sensation one gets when the stomach is empty and contractions of the stomach muscles come into play. Some obese people have a habit of eating even when this does not occur and they are not hungry. Very often a half hour after a full meal they raid the refrigerator or sit down to nibble on candy, pretzels, nuts, fruits or some other food. Eating any foods which contain sugar may produce hunger. You will find that when you eat a meal without a dessert you will not be hungry afterward. However, where a dessert is included in the meal, an hour or two later, the desire to nibble is present.

Appetite is a sensation one often gets when his sense of smell or sight comes in contact with food. For example, if one passes a bakery or confectionery shop and gets a smell of the cake or candy, he is likely to go into the shop and purchase something even though he had no such inclination a few minutes before. On the other hand, had he not passed the shop his appetite would not have been stimulated.

DIET IN OBESITY:

Many and various diets have been advocated for weight reduction. Newspapers, magazines, radio and T.V. programs have sponsored diets. Nutrition quacks preach diets for weight reduction. These have little reliability. A diet must be "measured" to an individual person's needs. It must be nutritionally sound and so constructed that the person using it will remain in good health although losing weight.

Your doctor is able to calculate a diet that will take into consideration your sex, age, height, occupation, and emotional make-up. A diet given to a twenty-two year old female school-teacher who is 5'1" tall would hardly fit the needs of a forty-year old piano mover who is 6' tall.

The average American diet consists of protein, 10 to 15 percent, carbohydrates, 50 to 60 percent, and fats 30 to 40 percent. Again the doctor would make changes to fit the needs of each patient. A good reducing diet would be protein — 50 to 60 percent, carbohydrates — 30 to 40 percent, and fat — 10 to 15 percent.

High protein diets have been advertised as "healthful diets." Do they aid in the loss of weight? This idea is a fallacy. One should not consume meat, fish or eggs at every meal. This could get monotonous in a short time, as well as being expensive. A well balanced diet of all essential foods is more palatable, less costly, and more interesting. Protein cereals, protein bread and protein meat is just so much hogwash. One gets all the protein he needs by eating meat (10-35%), fish (10-20%), eggs (10-12%), cheeses (15-30%), milk (4-8.5%), and dried beans (5-20%). In parentheses after each of the foods is the percentage of proteins that is found in them. You can readily see that four ounces of meat or four ounces of fish doesn't mean four ounces of protein. Only about 1/5 of the food element is protein. The rest is fat and water and in beans about 1/10 is protein and the rest carbohydrates and water.

All types of diets have been advocated for weight loss. Most of these diets are published in magazines, newspapers, and other media. The people for whom these diets are intended have never been interviewed, seen or examined by the diet proposers. These diets are circulated as "gimmicks" to increase the circulation of the periodicals. Many of them have been harmful to some people. To name a few fad diets: Milk and Banana diet, Mayo Clinic diet, Pot Cheese and Pineapple diet, Milk and Ice Cream diet, Milk and Fruit diet, Tomato Juice diet, Grape diet, formulæ and other liquid diets.

DRUGS

Here too, the faddists and the quacks have been on the rampage. They may come to you by knocking on your door, over television or radio, or through newspaper and magazine advertisements. No one should take any medication, not even an innocent looking vitamin pill, without consulting a doctor. These innocent little pills may be "loaded" with some drug to which you might be sensitive. Your doctor is the only one who can examine you and prescribe for your needs. Many people buy appetite appeasers such as candies, caramels, chewing gum, food preparations and bulk reducing drugs. All of these are advertised as aids to help you lose weight. Fortunately, the only thing most of us lose is the money we spend on them.

EXERCISE

Putting muscles to work is important because this activity helps to burn up calories. It also helps to tighten the particular muscles which are activated, reducing their measurements. Exercise has a beneficial effect on circulation and nutrition as well.

To lose one pound, one has to expend 3500 calories. Suppose a housewife who does her usual chores such as cleaning, washing, shopping, taking care of children and so forth uses up 2500 calories a day. Then she eats her three square meals a day, with a little nibbling in between, and a few TV or midnight snacks. She consumes about 3000 calories this way. What has happened? She has consumed 500 calories a day more than she burned. If she does this every day for a week, she will consume

7 x 500 calories or 3500 calories. This would be just the amount needed to give her an extra pound of weight. If, instead, she added 116 extra calories a day to the 2500 calories, it would take her a month to gain that extra pound. 116 x 30 days = 3480 calories. Remember, 3500 extra calories means one extra pound of fat on the hips or elsewhere.

Just what is a calorie? It is a unit of measure. If twenty drops of water are heated to the point where the temperature goes up one degree in a thermometer, you have one calorie. Scientifically speaking, a calorie is the amount of heat needed to raise one kilogram of water one degree centigrade. The energy or fuel value of food is measured in terms of these heat units, or calories. One gram of protein equals four calories. One gram of carbohydrate equals four calories. One gram of fat equals nine calories. Light exercise such as walking instead of using the car every time you have to go four or five blocks may help in burning up some of these calories.

If a person has more than ten pounds to lose, he should put himself under the care of a physician. A complete physical examination will be done. Tests will be made to determine if any pathology is present which is not connected with the obesity. These may include a basal metabolism test, urine test, blood tests and an electrocardiogram if necessary. The amount of weight he has to lose in order to keep him in caloric balance will be determined by the physician. Once his normal weight is maintained for a sufficient period of time, which may be from six months to a year, the chances are that he will keep his weight down for a long time. Chemical changes will occur in the liver, intestines and other tissues which will put him in chemical balance to accommodate the reduced weight.

MASSAGE

In the treatment of weight reducing, massage is useless. You neither lose weight nor take off inches by massage. On the contrary, the chance of acquiring loose muscles and loose skin is very good if massage is used frequently. The only way to tighten a muscle is by putting it to work.

DIETARY PROGRAM FOR OBESITY

To reduce the obese individual it is necessary to establish a negative energy balance (the daily caloric intake must be less than the daily energy output). A gradual loss of weight (6-8 lbs. monthly) can be achieved by a diet which yields 1000 calories less than the daily requirement. Effective diets for moderately active individuals range from 1200 to 1500 calories per day. More rapid weight loss is not usually desirable. Foods high in protein and fat remain in the stomach longer. Therefore, the protein allowance should be divided approximately equally among the three meals. Smaller meals and even between meal snacks may be eaten provided the total caloric allowance is not exceeded. It is essential that the obese individual realize that portions must be limited. The purpose of many diets has been defeated by excessive intake of allowed foods.

GENERAL RULES FOR EATING

1. Avoid excessive portions of any food.

2. Mineral oil dressings are especially to be avoided. They interfere with the absorption of vitamins A and D.

3. The caloric content of alcoholic beverages is high and their nutrient value non-existent. Therefore, they should be used very sparingly.

4. Bulk fillers and other appetite depressants are widely advertised and available without prescriptions. Do not be mis-

led by these facts into assuming that they are helpful. Bulk fillers have no effect and the action of appetite depressants is only temporary. Many may cause serious damage to some individuals. *Check with your physician before using any of these products.*

5.   4 grams..1 teaspoon
     3 teaspoons....,...1 tablespoon
     2 tablespoons..1 ounce
     8 ounces..1 cup or glass
     16 ounces (2 cups)..................................1 pint or 1 pound

All measures are based on standard measuring cups and spoons.

HOW TO CALCULATE A REDUCING DIET

The following table will aid you in finding the number of calories per day needed to lose an average of 2 pounds a week. Determine your desirable weight from the HEIGHT-WEIGHT CHART. Multiply your desirable weight by the correct figure in the table below. Subtract 1000 calories from the result and the balance will be the amount to follow daily.

Example: A stenographer weighing 135 pounds, multiply by 16 — 2160
                                                                      subtract — 1000
            Total number of calories to be consumed per day — 1160

	CALORIES	
	WOMEN	MEN
At work but sitting most of day: student, proofreader	15	16
Work done chiefly sitting: stenographer, bookkeeper, draftsman, teacher, musician	16	17
Standing or walking: salesman, dentist, physician, artist	17	18
Work developing muscular strength: plumber, painter, farmer, housewife without domestic help	20	22
Work requiring heavy labor: mover, lumberjack, road builder, bricklayer	—	23

The diet should be made up to include foods as follows: Proteins, 60% to 70%; Carbohydrates, 30% to 40%; Fats, 10% to 15%.

UNDERWEIGHT

A great deal has been written and said about obesity and overweight but very little work has been done on the subject of underweight. There are two types of lean individuals. One is of normal good health, possessing a good musculature, physical endurance and emotional stability. This individual is classed as the "sthenic" type and his thinness is usually inherited. He can eat as much or more than his obese prototype without adding an ounce of weight over his lifetime. There is some unknown factor involved in his chemistry of digestion which makes it possible for him to eat large quantities of foods or rich desserts and never gain weight.

There is another group of individuals who are known as the "asthenic" type. A person in this classification is not only thin but undernourished. He doesn't look like a healthy individual. He is always tired, has poor musculature, lacks physical endurance and is usually quite nervous. His appetite is poor and his meals are skimpy and nutritionally inadequate.

Very little, if anything, can be done to increase the weight of the sthenic type of person. However, the asthenic type can be helped by submitting himself to a thorough clinical examination so that his physician can determine if there is some degree of undernutrition, whether diseases such as anorexia nervosa or Simmonds disease is present. Whatever deficiency or clinical entity may be found, it will bear treatment with proper medication and diet. It may be necessary to increase the caloric intake of his diet by fifty per cent or more. The proportion of essential nutrients in the diet will have to be calculated to improve the well-being and emotional status of the individual.

Chapter Fourteen

DIABETES

Diabetes is a disease of metabolism and is characterized by a decrease in the secretion of insulin, which is a hormone from the pancreas gland. As a result of this, there is a breakdown in the metabolism of carbohydrates (sugar and starch). Sugar is stored in the blood and is excreted in the urine, thereby making it easy to detect by examining the blood or by doing a urinalysis. The disease frequently follows an hereditary pattern and often the individual is ignorant of any inherited background tendencies. Certain conditions arise which may be responsible for the breakdown in the metabolism and bring the diabetes to light. These are infectious diseases, worry and nervous tension. Overeating, resulting in obesity, is one of the chief predisposing causes. The first manifestations that may appear are frequent, short, copious urination, increased thirst, excessive hunger, a feeling of apathy and sometimes loss of weight.

Diabetes occurs mostly in the 50 to 70 year age groups. However, it is found in persons of all ages, including children. A diabetic must be under the supervision of a physician. The diet prescribed will be in accordance with the severity of the disease. Diabetes occurs twice as frequently in the female as the male in the older age group. In younger age groups it occurs in an even proportion of both sexes. Medication, such as insulin, which has to be taken by injection or a drug by mouth, may be necessary to help control the disease. At this time we do not have any drug which can be taken by mouth to control the disease in children. It is unfortunate that they have to take an injection of insulin daily. These patients must undergo an educational program by their doctor which is as important as the medication used. Before insulin was discovered diabetes was looked upon as a fatal disease. This is no longer true. Today, one may have the same life expectancy as any other healthy individual if (1) the educational program is taken seriously, (2) the diet is observed religiously, and (3) the medication is taken as prescribed. Even surgery can safely be performed on diabetics today as long as they are controlled by diet and medication.

The question often arises as to whether or not it is safe for a diabetic to get married. The offspring of two diabetic parents are likely to be diabetic. For this reason two diabetics should not get married. It may not even be wise for a man and woman neither of whom have diabetes, but each have one or more parents who are diabetic, to get married. However, a diabetic with no history of diabetes in the family may feel safe to marry a non-diabetic without any family history of diabetes. Offspring of such union are unlikely to have diabetes.

SUGGESTIONS FOR CONSIDERATION IN EDUCATION OF DIABETIC PATIENTS

Adjustment can be made by the physician to allow for occupation, hours of employment and eating facilities at work. Many problems must be solved by the physician and the patient. For example: The diabetic male who is employed on a rotating shift will necessarily eat his meals at different times each week.

National and religious food habits play an important part in the life of the diabetic as well as other individuals. These should and can be taken into consideration.*

Wide fluctuations in activity or routine (such as the difference in a working or school day and week-end) may necessitate an alternate meal plan for the individual. This should include approximately the same size meal at approximately the same time every day.

The omission of any meal is one of the main handicaps to good control. If it is impossible to eat all of the food allowed at a meal, the uneaten carbohydrate should be replaced by an equivalent amount of fruit juice.

When eating in a restaurant, it is possible for the diabetic to follow his meal plan. However, it is essential that he avoid high caloric desserts, sauces, gravies, casseroles and other foods of unknown composition. When traveling, the same rules apply except that the situation may be complicated by irregular stops for food. In that case it is recommended that he carry a "box lunch" or at least a carbohydrate supplement (fresh fruit, fruit juice or cube sugar).

The diabetic may feel that alcohol is essential to his comfort and well-being. It is not recommended and should be permitted only at the discretion of the physician who has the responsibility of being specific both as to the type and amount to be consumed. He should bear two points in mind: (1) Beer, sweet wines and mixed drinks fall into the category of "foods of uncertain composition." (2) All alcoholic beverages yield 7 calories per gram of alcohol contained.

See List of Publications on Page 126.

Chapter Fifteen

THE CHOLESTEROL STORY

A great deal of controversial interest has been mounting as to whether animal or butter fats or both are producing a type of arteriosclerosis (hardening of the arteries), sometimes called atherosclerosis.

Cholesterol is a fat substance that is present in nearly all living tissue. It aids in regulating fat metabolism. However, when it is found in excessive amounts in the blood, there is a possibility of these fat droplets depositing themselves on the inside lining of the large and medium arteries. If the fat droplets pile on top of each other, they form masses or plaques large enough to narrow or occlude an artery. This may occur in any artery of the body, but there seems to be a tendency for it to occur more often in the cerebral (brain) arteries and the coronary (around the heart) arteries. In some instances it may be found in the peripheral (extremities) arteries. Blood cells accumulate on these plaques and help to close up the arteries by forming clots. The results of such a condition may lead to a paralytic stroke or coronary artery disease.

For many years this was considered or associated with the problems of aging, but present day research has shown that it is a result of abnormal fat metabolism. Cholesterol increase in the blood usually occurs after the age of thirty and is more prevalent in each decade of life that follows. We do not concern ourselves with blood cholesterol levels in children though high levels may occur even at birth or in young children on occasions.

Cholesterol is measured in milligrams per cent and exists normally in the blood from 150 mg. % to 280 mg. %. Research has shown that levels up to 280 mg. % show no relationship to atherosclerosis. Levels over 280 mg. % are believed to be related to atherosclerosis.

Blood cholesterol varies in individuals and in people in different areas of the world. For instance, persons who are always under tension and are excitable get a physiological rise in their serum cholesterol. In this country people who are obese and have more than 40% fat or more than 50% of carbohydrates in their diet show a high cholesterol count.

Cholesterol blood levels are usually reduced when severe restricted intake of fat is practiced. Different fats have different effects on blood cholesterol. We must distinguish between two types of fats in the diet. One is called saturated fats and the other unsaturated fats. It is the saturated fats (animal and butter fats) that contain cholesterol in increased amounts and are responsible for the occurrence of atherosclerosis. The foods which have a high cholesterol count are listed under FOODS NOT PERMITTED in the RESTRICTED CHOLESTEROL DIET.

Although the unsaturated fats contain no cholesterol, they have as many calories as the saturated fats, and both are good sources of energy. Unsaturated fats are of importance as food for persons with high cholesterol or in those who have had a coronary attack or cerebral vascular accident because they may produce significant reductions in the serum cholesterol. These are corn oil, safflower oil, and cottonseed oil. Addition of a vegetable oil to the usual fat intake is ineffective. While no evidence is available, there is a feeling among the medical profession that an increased intake of vegetable oils may act as a prophylaxis for the general population in keeping the blood cholesterol at a low level.

Atherosclerosis appears most frequently in diabetes, hypothyroidism and obesity due to chemical and physical changes in the arteries. It has been demonstrated that a reduction in weight in the obese individual shows a lowering of the blood cholesterol level in those with initially elevated levels.

No person should be concerned or frightened by the statements appearing in newspapers, magazines and other media regarding cholesterol; that is unless they have had a recent blood test indicating an abnormal cholesterol level. It might be a good thing for any person over the age of 30 years to have a blood cholesterol test each birthday. Such information will help you to add years onto your life span. What a birthday present!

RESTRICTED CHOLESTEROL DIET*

GENERAL RULES: *No foods are to be creamed, buttered or fried, unless vegetable oils are used and not reused. Gas-forming vegetables should be avoided.*

	FOODS PERMITTED	FOODS NOT PERMITTED
BEVERAGES	Skim milk or butter-milk made from skim milk — include 2 cups daily. Tea, coffee.	Whole milk and whole milk drinks. Alcohol.
BREAD AND CEREALS	Whole grain or enriched bread and cereals. Saltines, soda and graham crackers — include 4 servings daily.	Crackers containing butter. Griddle cakes, waffles and doughnuts. All others.
CHEESE	Skim milk cottage cheese without added cream.	All others.
DESSERTS	Angel food cake, gelatin, puddings made with skim milk and no egg. Water ices.	Pastry, pie, cakes containing egg yolk, butter, whole milk, cream cheese, cream, chocolate. Puddings containing whole milk and eggs. Ice cream, sherbets.
EGGS	Whites only.	Egg yolk.
FATS	Vegetable oils and vegetable oil salad dressings.	Cream, butter, lard, bacon fat, chicken fat, margarine, solid vegetable shortenings.
FRUITS	All fresh, frozen or canned — include 1 to 2 servings daily (½ cup each) and 1 serving (¾ cup) citrus fruit.	None.
MEAT, FISH, POULTRY	Lean beef, lamb, veal, pork, ham, lean chicken or turkey (no skin). Lean white fish, haddock, flounder, fresh salmon, fresh cod — include 8 ounces daily.	Liver, brains, sweet-breads, giblets, tripe heart, kidney, bacon, sausage, oysters, shrimp, crabmeat, lobster, caviar, fish roe, duck, goose, luncheon meats, frankfurters.

	FOODS PERMITTED	FOODS NOT PERMITTED
MISC.	Fried foods in unused vegetable oils. Zero Dressing.** Vegetable oil salad dressings.	Foods fried in other than vegetable oils, gravies, cream and other sauces, nuts, chocolate, olives, coconut, mayonnaise.
POTATO AND SUBSTITUTES	Potato (white or sweet), rice, macaroni, spaghetti, plain noodles — include 1 potato daily.	Egg noodles.
SOUPS	Broth, clear soups and vegetable soups with all fat removed.	Cream soups.
SWEETS	Jelly, sugar, honey, hard candy, jam, marmalade, preserves.	Chocolate and all other candy.
VEGETABLES	All fresh, canned or frozen — include 3-4 servings (½ cup each) 1 dark green, 1 yellow, and 1 raw.	Restricted on advice of physician: broccoli, brussels sprouts, cabbage, cauliflower, cucumber, onions, radishes, turnips, dried beans, peas and lentils.

SUGGESTED MEAL PLAN
(Subject to caloric regulations)

BREAKFAST	LUNCH	DINNER
Fruit	Lean meat, fish or poultry	Lean meat, fish or poultry
Cereal with skim milk	Potato or substitute	Potato or substitute
Toast with jelly	Vegetable	Vegetable
Beverage	Fruit	Salad with Zero Dressing**
	Bread with jelly	Dessert of fruit
	Beverage	Bread with jelly
		Beverage

**ZERO SALAD DRESSING RECIPE

(Cholesterol-free Dressing)
(May be used in any amount)
½ cup tomato juice
2 tbsps. lemon juice or vinegar
1 tbsp. onion, finely chopped
Salt and pepper

Chopped parsley or green pepper, horse-radish, or mustard may be added if desired. Combine ingredients in a jar with a tightly fitted top. Shake well before using.

New Jersey Department of Health — Diet Manual (1960).

Chapter Sixteen

FOODS, FADS AND FALLACIES

The charlatans and the quacks are having a Roman holiday today. In years gone by, they stood on the street corners or on trucks and "peddled" medicines and herbs to an audience of ten or twenty people. Today, with our tremendous system of communication, they reach into millions of homes. Television, radio, newspapers, magazines and lecture tours are media utilized to spread their propaganda and mulct the American people of a half billion dollars a year. The charlatan or medicine man can spread his information in a style so convincing that many accept his word as authentic. He labels himself as "Dr." so and so, nutrition authority. He publishes books and periodicals with such catchy titles as, "How To Keep From Looking Older Than Your Husband," "How To Get Rid Of Your Fat And Conquer Hollywood," "Cancer Cured In 10 Easy Lessons," "Arthritis Is For The Birds — Are You A Bird," "To Cure Anemia Put Your Blood To Sleep Every Night," "How To Use Black Strap Molasses And Pigeon Milk To Give You That Baby Complexion." These writings give him a badge of authority. The fact that these books are sprinkled with some references from reliable experts, interspersed with the writer's own brand of misinformation tucked in between the lines, is not recognized by the reader.

Pills consisting of vitamins or other drugs, chewing gum with aromatic oils, and food fads are advocated for "weight reducing," "arthritis," and for "blood that is weary." The customer buys these from mail order drug and food houses, only to find that they are worthless for his particular complaint or ailment. The money back guarantee is seldom used by the customer because he hates to admit that someone made a fool of him. They may come knocking on your door with cures for anything from ingrown toenails to falling hair. Peculiar as it may seem, there is very little that any government agency can do to stop this. The reasons are that the government agencies, such as the Food and Drug Administration, the Federal Trade Commission, and the Post Office Department, which are our first line of defense, are greatly understaffed. Although the investigators which they employ are excellent and do a thorough job, it is impossible for the government to prosecute and get a conviction in every case of misleading advertisement, false claims and fraud. The legal departments of these agencies are usually staffed by young lawyers with little experience in trial work, while the defendant drug houses have a battery of highly trained lawyers to defend their cases. The drug companies take appeal after appeal when the government does win a case. These appeals and trials may go from one court to another for many years and during all this time the drug in question is still on the market and still being sold. Ethical drug manufacturers usually cooperate with the government agencies without resorting to court action.

It is unfortunate that vitamin supplements which are important and helpful for indicated conditions are misused and abused by the propaganda disseminated by these quacks. They have made worthwhile preparations become worthless by advocating their use for everything under the sun.

The hodge podge and confusion in which people looking for the "Fountain of Youth" find themselves is pitiful. The charlatan, nutrition quack or food faddist takes advantage of this situation. Before buying any of these products call your local Medical Society or write to the American Medical Association, 535 North Dearborn Street, Chicago, Illinois, for reliable information.

Be sensible and use your money to insure good nutrition and good health by seeing your doctor if and when you feel there is something wrong. Don't buy empty promises.

FACTS OR FALLACIES

1. Q. *Does a lot of water flush the kidneys?*
    A. No. Water is essential for life. Excessive amounts do neither harm nor good.

2. Q. *Is water fattening?*
    A. It contains no calories and is not converted to body fat; ⅔ of total body weight is water.

3. Q. *Does salt produce high blood pressure?*
    A. No. Salt is essential for health. There is no danger in moderate amounts. People who have high blood pressure do not tolerate salt but, in itself, it does not produce an increased blood pressure.

4. Q. *Are large amounts of roughage necessary for health?*
    A. Too much may be dangerous. Some people are even distressed by small amounts.

5. Q. *Are dry cereals necessary for body energy?*
    A. Dry cereals supply the same amount of energy as cooked cereals, potatoes, sugars or fats.

102

6. Q. *Is fasting one day a week healthy?*
   A. No. It may do no harm, but in some people it disturbs bodily functions.

7. Q. *Does a man doing hard labor need a high meat diet?*
   A. No. Muscular exercise demands an excessive supply of energy foods such as carbohydrates and vitamins in addition to other foods.

8. Q. *Are milk and cheese constipating?*
   A. No.

9. Q. *Is it safe to leave food standing in open tin cans?*
   A. Yes, if the food is properly refrigerated.

10. Q. *Are canned vegetables less nutritious than fresh cooked vegetables?*
    A. No. Both depend on the nutritive value of the original vegetable and the method of preparation.

11. Q. *Is baking soda harmful in cooking green vegetables?*
    A. Yes. It destroys the vitamins.

12. Q. *Does drinking water with meals retard digestion?*
    A. No. It aids digestion rather than hinders it.

13. Q. *Is it safe to eat acid fruits and milk together?*
    A. Yes. Milk is curdled as soon as it comes in contact with the digestive juices in the stomach.

14. Q. *Are fish and celery brain food?*
    A. No.

15. Q. *Is black strap molasses good for anemia and arthritis?*
    A. No. The iron contained in this is rust scraped from machinery that is used in the manufacture of sugar. Some vitamins are present which exist in most foods. It is used mainly as a feed for livestock.

16. Q. *Are raw eggs more digestible than cooked ones?*
    A. No. Soft or hard boiled eggs are more digestible than raw eggs.

17. Q. *Are white eggs more nutritious than brown eggs?*
    A. No. Color is no indicator of nutritional value.

18. Q. *Is it harmful to eat eggs every day?*
    A. One or two eggs are not harmful to any healthy person. In some diseases, however, eggs may have to be eliminated from the diet.

19. Q. *Is coffee bad for people who have high blood pressure?*
    A. There is a tendency for the caffeine in the coffee to lower a high blood pressure about 45 minutes after it is taken. Caffeine dilates the blood vessels around the heart and increases the amount of oxygen which reaches the heart muscle.

20. Q. *Will raw eggs or raw oysters increase sexual potency?*
    A. No.

21. Q. *Should eggs form an important part of the diet of older people?*
    A. No. The yolk of eggs contains a substance which tends to produce hardening of the arteries. However, in persons with a normal cholesterol level, there is no harm in eating eggs.

22. Q. *Will an apple a day keep the doctor away?*
    A. No.

23. Q. *Which is more nutritious, butter or margarine?*
    A. They are both about the same. In most cases, margarine has added vitamins.

24. Q. *Are fresh peppers, green or red, harmful?*
    A. No. They are high in vitamin C.

25. Q. *Which has more calories, fresh bread or toast?*
    A. They both have the same amount of calories.

26. Q. *Is gelatin as good a source of protein as meat or fish?*
    A. No. Gelatin does not contain most of the essential amino acids to sustain life which are found in meat or fish. It is one of the inferior sources of protein.

27. Q. *Will gelatin make soft nails stronger and will it make them grow?*
    A. This is very questionable. These conditions of the nails may be due to a number of factors such as endocrine disturbances or poor nutrition.

28. Q. *Which makes the blood pressure rise, hot or cold foods?*
    A. Cold. Ice cream or iced beverages increase the blood pressure 15 or 20 points and also increase the pulse 18 to 20 beats per minute.

29. Q. *Is saccharine good for people on reducing diets?*
    A. No. The average saccharine tablet sold contains sodium which tends to hold fluids in the tissues, making it dif-

ficult to lose weight. However, there are some sweetening agents, including some saccharine, which contain calcium instead of sodium.

30. Q. *Is boiled milk constipating?*
    A. No.

31. Q. *Which is more digestible, raw milk or boiled milk?*
    A. Boiled milk.

32. Q. *Is yogurt a healthful food?*
    A. The same as milk, the same calories and the same food value.

33. Q. *The best time to eat candy is between meals. True or False?*
    A. False. The best time is at the end of the meal unless you are trying to lose weight, then not at all.

34. Q. *Is mineral oil a good laxative?*
    A. No. It interferes with absorption of vitamin A and D and also calcium and phosphorus.

35. Q. *Does pork liver have more iron than beef liver?*
    A. Yes. On the other hand, beef liver has more vitamin A than pork liver; otherwise they contain the same elements.

36. Q. *Vegetarians claim they get their protein from eating fruits and vegetables. Is this so?*
    A. These foods have inadequate amounts of protein and no complete proteins. However, most vegetarians get their needed proteins from grains, legumes and nuts; while some straddling vegetarians get their proteins from milk, cheese and eggs.

37. Q. *Does depleted soil give a poor nutritive crop?*
    A. No. The amount of size of the crop might be influenced by a poor soil, but not the nutritive value of the crop.

38. Q. *Are rare steaks and roast beef good for anemia?*
    A. Rare, medium or well done meats have the same nutritive value.

39. Q. *Are vegetable oils less fattening than butter or margarine?*
    A. No. Both the same.

40. Q. *Does butter have more calories than margarine?*
    A. No. Both the same.

41. Q. *Does frozen orange juice have less nutritive value than*

fresh orange juice?
A. No. Both contain the same amount of vitamin C.

42. Q. *Is high-protein bread a good substitute for meat, fish, or eggs?*
    A. No. All breads contain the same amount of protein. One would need eight slices of bread (not thin sliced) to get the same amount of protein as is contained in four ounces of meat. The protein in the bread comes from the milk or other foods of animal origin used as ingredients.

43. Q. *Is peanut butter a good source of protein?*
    A. Eight tablespoons of peanut butter supply about the same amount of protein as four ounces of meat.

44. Q. *Is it safe to cook acid foods in aluminun utensils?*
    A. Yes. There is no scientific proof that aluminum utensils are harmful when used in cooking acid foods.

45. Q. *Does an average portion of cottage cheese supply the same amount of calcium as a glass of milk?*
    A. One and one-half cups of cottage cheese have about the same amount of calcium as one glass of milk.

46. Q. *Are vitamins lost when the liquid is poured off from canned vegetables?*
    A. Yes. About one third of the vitamins and minerals are poured down the drain.

47. Q. *Is any food value lost in canned grapefruit and orange sections?*
    A. A very small amount of vitamin C is lost in canning and storage.

48. Q. *Is there much difference between cane sugar and beet sugar?*
    A. No. They both have the same chemical composition.

49. Q. *Do skimmed milk cottage cheese and creamed cottage cheese have the same food value?*
    A. Both have the same value except that creamed cottage cheese has more fat and vitamin A.

50. Q. *Does fluorine in water really reduce cavities in teeth?*
    A. Yes. Scientific evidence has shown that the incidence of cavities has been considerably reduced when fluorine has been added to the drinking water.

Chapter Seventeen

NUTRITION

IN CHILDREN

To watch an infant grow into childhood and from childhood to the teens is not only a delight but a fascinating miracle. Let us start before birth. The unborn infant gets its nourishment through the afterbirth (placenta). This serves as a means of communication between the infant and the mother. For this reason it is very important for the expectant mother to get proper nutrition from foods and supplements so that she can have a healthy newborn child.

The foodstuff most responsible for this growth is protein; without it there would be no growth. In fact, without it there would be no life. Foods rich in protein are milk, eggs, fish, meat, beans, peas and nuts. There is, sometimes, a tendency for the expectant mother to eliminate from her diet some of these essential foods, together with others, either because she is afraid she may gain too much weight or because they may produce some nausea or vomiting. (This may be called a psychic allergic manifestation).

Every effort should be made by the expectant mother to eat not only the foods rich in protein but foods high in vitamin A. This vitamin is important to aid the growth and strength of the bones in the fetus, to strengthen the cells and tissues which make up the eyes and to prevent anomalies in the fetus such as cleft palate (an opening between the palate and the roof of the mouth). The diet of the expectant mother should include all the foods found in the Basic Four Groups (see page 77). She should have milk as a beverage four times a day in preference to tea, coffee or soda. And in addition, she should take a vitamin-mineral supplement which has some folic acid in it.

During infancy and in the years to follow it is important that the child has a sufficient amount of sleep, play and exercise which contribute to the process of growth. During play and exercise, children expend a tremendous amount of energy, much more than an adult. This continual drive comes from the food they eat. The food provides them with a storehouse of energy. The body activity usually comes from the carbohydrates they consume. Foods containing these carbohydrates are starch and sugars such as bread, cereal, potatoes, beans, peas, corn, fruits, honey and molasses.

Fats provide children with heat and power that increase their activities. Foods rich in fats are milk, cream, cheese, butter, bacon, meat, fish, eggs, and peanut butter.

Calcium is a mineral that plays an important part in the growth and development of the child. When a sufficient amount of this mineral is deposited in his bones, it contributes to the strength and support of these bones. With this reinforcement he learns to stand and walk erect. His spinal column becomes strong and sturdy, providing him with a very good foundation to support his body. Foods containing calcium are milk, cheese, eggs, whole grain bread, cereal, fruit, vegetables (leafy green), carrots and dry beans.

Vitamins are essential to health and growth in children. Some vitamins are designated by alphabetical letters — A, B, B_2, C, E, D and G, while others have names such as ascorbic acid, niacin and thiamine.

Vitamin A helps the eyes to adjust from bright light to darkness in a short time. It also keeps the tissues and sensitive membranes in healthy condition, provides the body with a certain amount of protection against infections and contributes to growth and the formation of good teeth.

Vitamin B promotes the health of nerves and muscles and aids in toning up the digestive tract.

Vitamin B_2 is essential for growth and for preventing formation of fissures or cracks in the corners of the mouth and eyelids.

Vitamin C strengthens the walls of the small blood vessels, thus preventing fragility. It also helps in producing strong teeth and bones.

Vitamin D is a preventive of rickets, a disease of infancy or childhood from which bone deformities such as bowlegs, bulging forehead and malformation of chest and ribs often result.

GENERAL RULES FOR FEEDING CHILDREN

1. The consistency of foods should be governed by age and development of the child. Progress toward whole foods should be made as soon as possible.

2. Size of portion varies with age, development and appetite of the child. (Appetite is greater during the first twelve months than it is the second year inasmuch as growth is not as rapid during this latter period.)

3. A child should not be forced to eat. A child who does not eat well should not be fed between meals.

4. In introducing new foods, give a small amount at first at the beginning of the meal when a child is hungry. Only one new food should be introduced at a time. Do not introduce it if a child is not feeling well.

5. If a new food is rejected, do not make an issue of it. Try again in several days.

FOODS THAT WILL MEET NEEDS OF HEALTHY CHILDREN*
DIET FROM 1 - 6

FOOD	APPROXIMATE QUANTITY NEEDED DAILY	AVERAGE SIZE SERVING FOR EACH AGE		
		1 YEAR	2 & 3 YEARS	4 & 5 YEARS
Milk to drink and in or on food	3 to 4 measuring cups	½-1 cup	½-1 cup	1 cup
Bread, whole grain or enriched	1½-3 slices	½-1 slice	1 slice	1-1½ slices
Cereal, whole grain enriched or restored	1 serving	¼ cup	½ cup	½ cup
Butter or fortified margarine	Spread on bread and used on vegetables			
Eggs	1	1	1	1
Fruit for Vitamin C	1 medium orange or ⅓ cup citrus or ⅔ cup tomato juice	⅓-½ cup	⅓-½ cup	⅓-½ cup
Other fruit (apples, apricots, bananas, peaches, pears, prunes, most berries)	1 serving	¼ cup	⅓ cup	½ cup
Meat, poultry, fish, cottage cheese	1-4 tbsps.	1 tbsp.	2-3 tbsps.	4 tbsps.
Potatoes, white or sweet	1 serving	2 tbsps.	3 tbsps.	4 tbsps.
Raw vegetables (carrots, cabbage, tomatoes, lettuce, etc.)	1 serving			
Other cooked vegetables (mostly green leafy or deep yellow ones)	1-2 servings	2 tbsps.	3 tbsps.	3-4 tbsps.

Your Child From One-Six, Children's Bureau, U. S. Department of Health, Education and Welfare.

6. Very young or very active children may need between meal feedings. These should be fruit or juice, milk, cubes of lean meat or cheese, rather than cookies or candy snacks.
7. Sweets should be given only at the end of a meal. Sweets depress appetite and may take the place of foods the body needs. Sweets should not be used as a bribe — this will make them more appealing.
8. Vitamin supplements should be given *only* on the order of a physician.

IN TEENAGERS

Teenagers are a distinct class in themselves. They are an in-between group with adult standards and rules of conduct. Girls do not rate as high a nutrition quotient as boys of this age because too often they are more interested in their appearances and make-up than they are in food. Many of them go with little or no breakfast and often a coke suffices for lunch. Boys on the other hand are interested in athletics and other activities in which a great deal of energy is expended and this calls for increased amounts of varied foods.

Neither sex, as a rule, gets enough nutrients. Many do not drink sufficient quantities of milk, instead they drink sodas. A teenager should have at least four glasses of milk a day. This may be either whole milk or skim milk. They need the extra calcium to build and repair bones, muscles and nerves. Milk also supplies protein which aids in the building and repairing of body tissues and vitamin B_2 (riboflavin) which helps convert food into energy.

Teenagers should eat more vegetables. They need the green and yellow vegetables which are high in vitamin A, but they usually omit them from their meals. Vitamin A is necessary for a glowing complexion and it is needed for good vision. Citrus fruits, tomatoes and raw cabbage, which are all high in vitamin C, are often missing from the teenage diet. Vitamin C helps to prevent fatigue and together both vitamins help resist infection. Four or more servings of the A and C foods should be included in the daily diet.

Many of the teenagers — particularly the girls — are breakfast skippers. They rush off to school without a morsel of food because they devote too much time to doing their hair and putting on their make-up. Getting up a half hour earlier each morning would give them time to have orange juice, cereal, toast, an egg and milk. They do not realize it but a hearty breakfast would get them through their studies or work in the morning without that 10 or 11 o'clock fatigue. They need that extra energy which they can get only from a good breakfast.

A hot dog and a coke, favorite foods of teenagers, are inadequate as a luncheon. A good sandwich, glass of milk and a piece of fruit would furnish energy for them in the afternoon. Their dinner should consist of meat or fish, a generous portion of green and yellow vegetables and a glass of milk.

IN THE AGED

The writer recently had the privilege of being a delegate to the White House Conference on Aging where the subject of nutrition and physical fitness in this group received considerable attention. The objectives were to promote additional research in detecting nutritional failure in the aging and toward the proper application of advanced nutritional therapy. With this in mind it was postulated that instead of retiring a person at age 65 as it is done today, perhaps this could be delayed 10 or 15 years. With proper nutrition many of the degenerative diseases could be retarded. Lifelong indiscretions in diet are manifested in the aged. We may see a person at 60 who is feeble, frail, slow moving and dulled in sensibilities. Yet we often find one of 80 who is quite the reverse. He may be strong, well constructed, alert and keen of mind. Physical fitness is more important than chronological age. The difference between malnutrition and good nutrition from youth-hood to adult-hood is what determines the display of stamina in the aged.

The various senses diminish with aging such as the senses of sight, hearing and taste, thereby lessening the desire or ability to read, listen to music and enjoy food. Artificial dentures which do not fit properly, sensitive teeth, or diseased gums may play an important part in the refusal to eat proper foods, thus promoting digestive disturbances which become uncomfortable and sometimes unbearable.

The loss of a mate, having to live with and becoming dependent upon a child or relative, or finding themselves in a public or private home for the aged may precipitate an emotional upset. The result may be a feeling of insecurity which brings with it a depression and a loss of interest in the pleasure of living. This psychic manifestation tends to bring about a state of inadequate nutrition.

There is a 7.5% reduction in daily caloric requirements for each decade between 45 and 65 years. For example: at age 45, the daily requirement is 3,000 calories; then at age 55, it would be 7.5% less (225 calories) or 2,775 calories. At age 65, it would be 2,550 calories. The diet must include an extra amount of essential food elements to overcome the reduction in appetite which may be present.

It is important that the protein content should not be reduced. Calcium-containing foods should be increased through the use of extra milk and milk products to prevent softening or porousness of the bones which make them susceptible to fractures. B vitamins may spare this group from chronic fatigue because in reducing the caloric intake they get less of the B complex from the lessened intake of essential foods.

An elderly person living alone may not have the desire to prepare three full meals a day just for himself. Frequent light snacks and perhaps some hot milk at bedtime should be suggested because they will furnish a similar amount of nutrients.

The elderly should be encouraged to continue to do things which will stimulate physical and mental activities. By keeping physically fit and mentally alert not only will they get a personal satisfaction out of living but they will be able to contribute the fruits of their wisdom and experience to society.

SUGGESTIONS FOR MEAL PLANNING:

1. Serve every person normal adequate meals unless special food has been ordered by his doctor.
2. Plan each meal to be nutritionally adequate within itself so that it will furnish about one-third of the day's requirements.
3. Serve meals at regular hours and on time.
4. If it is impossible to serve supper and breakfast less than fourteen hours apart, include a bedtime snack consisting of protein foods such as a milk drink and/or a sandwich.
5. In modifying the diet to suit individual needs, change the preparation, not the foods.
   a. Cube, chop or grind foods that are difficult to chew.
   b. Casserole dishes are easy to eat and have appeal.
   c. Cooked fruits and vegetables are softer than fresh.
6. Make meals appetizing by including some food of distinctive flavor to contrast with softer foods; and some bright colored food for eye appeal.

7. If mineral oil is taken for medicinal purposes, do not give it until at least 4 hours after supper. Mineral oil interferes with the absorption of fat soluble vitamins (A and D) from foods.

MAN IN SPACE

Whether flights into space will be of short or long duration, food must be considered an important item on the itinerary. If a man is to survive in space travel, he must choose his food wisely. He must also devise a vehicle from which he can be ejected safely into outer space. He may travel to the moon and to different planets, and for this reason knowledge must be acquired as to how we can get him safely back to earth. The longer the duration of the flight, the more complicated the nutritional program appears. If one is preparing for an overnight flight and return trip, the preparation for food supply will be meager. However, if a flight is contemplated that will last several months or even several years, many factors have to be considered. Thought must be given to the weight of the individual, the food he carries, equipment, and utensils.

Oxygen and water, important elements of food, are necessary for maintaining good nutrition. It has been calculated that the weight of oxygen used by man is about 1½ pounds a day or approximately 550 pounds a year. Man needs 2.2 quarts of water each day. This means that for one year almost a ton of water per man would have to be carried. Can you imagine what a problem this could create if a group of ten, twenty, or fifty people went on the same flight for an extended period of time? It has also been estimated that the average person at home consumes about five or six pounds of food a day. People like to eat well when they are traveling. Just the thought of going on a cruise suggests a sumptuous cuisine. Dining cars on trains serve a variety of foods. Airplanes of today serve delicious meals which often include alcoholic beverages. Since liquors have weight, they may have to be abandoned in space travel.

As a prelude to space flight, research was conducted by the Aero Medical Laboratory, Wright Air Development Center, Ohio, and was reported by Beatrice Finkelstein and Lt. Col. H. A. Taylor in *Military Medicine* of October, 1959, and again by B. Finkelstein in the April, 1960 Journal of the *American Dietetic Association*. Studies were made for simulated five-day flights. These were done for high altitude balloon flights, for dark isolation trials, and for liquid diets which might be used in short space flights of the future.

Menus will probably be of the fluid type in squeeze bottles connected by tube to the mouth through the mask. A liquid high protein diet of about one hundred grams a day and twenty-five hundred calories per man has been recommended as feasible. It could consist of fruit and vegetable juices, a protein supplement beef drink, chocolate milk and concentrated ice cream mix. With the use of liquid foods under gravity-free conditions, measures must be taken to prevent aspiration of the diet into the lungs. Feeding personnel in high performance aircraft and in space travel poses other problems. There will be a need for more and varied concentrated foods, advances in cold sterilization of foods, improved methods of packaging, and development of lightweight food service equipment.

Professor Jack Myers of Texas University investigated the possibility of using oxygen-producing algae as a food for space travel. Others who have been doing research in this field have reported in *Nutrition Reviews,* the journal of the Nutrition Foundation, how some of these feeding problems may be solved. They studied two groups of five men who were maintained in the confined limits of a crew compartment for fifteen days, and thirty-five individuals who were maintained in a dark sound-proof chamber from six to one hundred and sixty-eight hours. In these studies it was found possible to provide adequate nourishment under simulated conditions of space travel to which crews of space vehicles would be subjected.

Our present knowledge of celestial mechanics for maintaining good nutrition for spacemen is vague. However, as new techniques of propulsion develop to carry man beyond the magnetic field, we will learn the answers to many questions. The construction of our present space vehicles does not allow man to move about; instead he must lie in a confined space. It has been demonstrated also that the noise involved in the movement of these vehicles is constant, causing insomnia to be common. With these and other problems to be solved, one can readily understand that there is a great deal of research yet to be done to provide for the comfort and well-being of man in space travel.

SIGNS OF MALNUTRITION

1. TIREDNESS

2. HAIR
    a. Dry
    b. Falls out easily

3. EYES
    a. Red, dry lids
    b. Inflammation of lids
    c. Fissures at angles
        of lids
    d. Night blindness

4. MOUTH
    a. Fissures at angles
        of mouth
    b. Ulcers of the mouth
    c. Extreme redness of
        tongue
    d. Deep wide grooves on
        the tongue
    e. Caries in teeth
    f. Bleeding gums
    g. Swelling gums

5. SKIN
    a. Oily
    b. Red
    c. Dry
    d. Scaly
    e. Black and blue areas
        (not due to trauma)
    f. Pigmentation
    g. Chicken skin
    h. Spider web
    i. Blood vessels
    j. Cold hands and feet
    k. Burning of hands
        and feet
    l. Redness of the palms
        of hands
    m. Brittle or soft nails

6. MUSCLE AND BONES
    a. Numbness of fingers
        and toes
    b. Pain in calf
    c. Bowlegs
    d. Flaring ribs
    e. Thickening of breast
        bone
    f. Pot belly
    g. Poor posture
    h. Swelling of legs

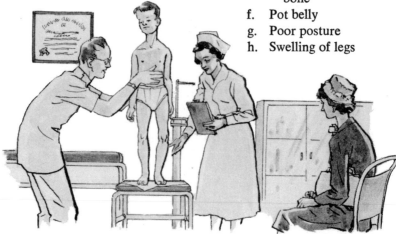

Chapter Eighteen

SOME STATISTICS AND STANDARDS

HERE IS WHAT YOU ARE CHEMICALLY:
An approximate analysis of a 150 lb. man — 5′ 8″ in height:

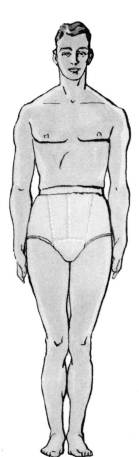

OXYGEN	92½ lbs.
CARBON	32 lbs.
HYDROGEN	15 lbs.
NITROGEN	5 lbs.
CALCIUM	3 lbs.
PHOSPHORUS	1¼ lbs.
POTASSIUM	4 oz.
SULFUR	2 oz.
SODIUM	1 oz.
CHLORINE	1 oz.
FLUORINE	½ oz.
MAGNESIUM	½ oz.
IODINE	A trace
IRON	A trace
COPPER	A trace
COBALT	A trace
MANGANESE	A trace
ZINC	A trace
SILICON	A trace

All of these are derived from the food we eat plus oxygen which
we breathe.

116 ENERGY EXPENDITURES:

Expended energy in calories depends on the amount of muscular activity or work done and the time that is utilized.

ACTIVITIES	YOU USE CALORIES PER POUND OF YOUR WEIGHT PER HOUR
Sleeping	½
Sitting	⅗
Standing	¾
Light exercise	1
Moderate exercise	1½
Active exercise	2
Severe exercise	3

EXAMPLE:

Person weighing 140 lbs. doing clerical work

Sleeping — 8 hours x ½ calorie per hour x 140 = 560
Sitting   — 8 hours x ⅗ calorie per hour x 140 = 672
Standing — 2 hours x ¾ calorie per hour x 140 = 210
Light exercise
or work — 6 hours x 1 calorie per hour x 140 = 840

Total calories expended   2282 calories

DAILY ENERGY REQUIREMENTS ACCORDING TO OCCUPATION:

	TOTAL CALORIES ALLOWED PER DAY		CALORIES PER LB. USED PER DAY	
	MEN	WOMEN	MEN	WOMEN
At work, but sitting most of day: student, proofreader	2000-2300	1600-1800	16	15

	TOTAL CALORIES ALLOWED PER DAY		CALORIES PER LB. USED PER DAY	
	MEN	WOMEN	MEN	WOMEN

Work done chiefly sitting: stenographer, bookkeeper, draftsman, teacher, musician, etc.

| 2200-2800 | 2000-2200 | 18 | 19 |

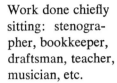

Standing or walking: salesman, dentist, physician, artist

| 2700-3000 | 2200-2500 | 20 | 21 |

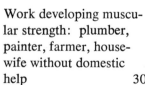

Work developing muscular strength: plumber, painter, farmer, housewife without domestic help

| 3000-3500 | 2000-2500 | 23 | 25 |

	TOTAL CALORIES ALLOWED PER DAY		CALORIES PER LB. USED PER DAY	
	MEN	WOMEN	MEN	WOMEN

Work requiring heavy labor: mover, lumberjack, road builder, bricklayer, etc.

	TOTAL CALORIES ALLOWED PER DAY		CALORIES PER LB. USED PER DAY	
	4000-6000	—	36	—

CORRECT MEASUREMENTS FOR WOMEN:

To determine the correct measurements do as follows: take the height measurement first.

The bust should measure thirty inches plus the number of inches over five feet.

The hip measurement should be two inches more than the bust measurement.

The waist measurement should be eight inches less than the bust measurement.

Example: If a person is five feet four inches tall, the bust measurement should be 30 plus 4 or 34 inches. The hip measurement will be 34 plus 2 or 36 inches. The waist measurement will be 34 minus 8 or 26 inches.

These figures apply to women who are normal weight for their age, height and build.

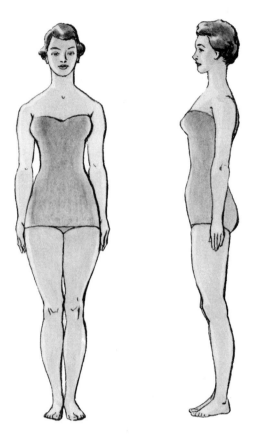

NEW WEIGHT STANDARDS FOR MEN AND WOMEN: *

In view of the importance of body weight to health and longevity, the findings of the Build and Blood Pressure Study, 1959, conducted by the Society of Actuaries, are of major significance. The study not only contributes new data on average heights and weights according to age, but also provides information from which new standards of desirable weight have been developed by the Statistical Bureau of the Metropolitan Life Insurance Company. These appear in table form.

The new tables of average weights differ in many respects from those now in common use, which were based on two similar studies of insured persons covering the periods 1885-1900 and 1909-27. For women, the new average weights are quite consistently less than they were in the earlier studies, while for men they tend to be higher than before. Thus, at age 25 the average weight for women is generally 5 to 6 pounds less than that shown in the last study; at age 35 it is from 2 to 4 pounds less, and at age 45 generally 2 to 3 pounds less. The decrease in average weights of women reflects chiefly their effort to keep slim and, to some extent, the lighter weight of their clothes.

Among men, the increase in average weight, compared with earlier standards, varies appreciably with height. The increase is greatest for short men, amounting to 5 pounds or more at most ages. For men of average height the increase is from 2 to 4 pounds, and for tall men from 1 to 3 pounds, the larger differences being found under age 45. Apparently the campaigns for weight control, to which women have clearly responded, have had much less impact on men.

The average weights in the present study rise with advance in age among both men and women, but the pattern differs somewhat for the two sexes. Among men, the averages rise rapidly during the 20's and early 30's, but the rate of increase then slackens off and is very small between the 40's and 50's. Among women, the increases in weight with age are fairly steady, but are most rapid between the mid-30's and mid-40's.

The new Build and Blood Pressure Study clearly shows that the lowest mortality generally occurs among people who are well below average weight. Even among young people, the advantage of a slight degree of overweight is less pronounced than in earlier studies, and at best can now be considered only a temporary advantage. At the middle and older ages, the results of the new study not only underscore the disadvantage of overweight, but also indicate that desirable weights, under current conditions, are somewhat lower than those shown in the tables prepared by the Metropolitan Life Insurance Company in the early 1940's.

Control of body weight, although not easily achieved, is of vital importance for the health and longevity of the American people. It involves a proper balance between food intake and expenditure of energy. For a large and increasing proportion of people, the daily tasks both on the job and at home have been greatly lightened by labor-saving devices. Automation promises to reduce still further the energy expended in many occupations, some of which had called for relatively heavy labor. Moreover, our leisure time is being spent increasingly in sedentary types of recreation. Accordingly, there is need for a change in the dietary habits of many adult Americans. Health education relating to nutrition, particularly in the schools, needs to be reoriented in some degree to emphasize the need for caloric balance in the diet in the light of modern living and working conditions. Regular exercise and active recreation of reasonable type and amount should be encouraged as an aid in weight control.

TABLE 1 — AVERAGE WEIGHTS FOR MEN AND WOMEN

According to Height and Age

HEIGHT
(In Shoes)   WEIGHT IN POUNDS (In Indoor Clothing)

MEN

HEIGHT	AGES 20-24	AGES 25-29	AGES 30-39	AGES 40-49	AGES 50-59	AGES 60-69
5′ 2″	128	134	137	140	142	139
3″	132	138	141	144	145	142
4″	136	141	145	148	149	146
5″	139	144	149	152	153	150
6″	142	148	153	156	157	154
7″	145	151	157	161	162	159
8″	149	155	161	165	166	163
9″	153	159	165	169	170	168
10″	157	163	170	174	175	173
11″	161	167	174	178	180	178
6′ 0″	166	172	179	183	185	183
1″	170	177	183	187	189	188
2″	174	182	188	192	194	193
3″	178	186	193	197	199	198
4″	181	190	199	203	205	204

WOMEN

HEIGHT	AGES 20-24	AGES 25-29	AGES 30-39	AGES 40-49	AGES 50-59	AGES 60-69
4′ 10″	102	107	115	122	125	127
11″	105	110	117	124	127	129
5′ 0″	108	113	120	127	130	131
1″	112	116	123	130	133	134
2″	115	119	126	133	136	137
3″	118	122	129	136	140	141
4″	121	125	132	140	144	145
5″	125	129	135	143	148	149
6″	129	133	139	147	152	153
7″	132	136	142	151	156	157
8″	136	140	146	155	160	161
9″	140	144	150	159	164	165
10″	144	148	154	164	169	*
11″	149	153	159	169	174	*
6′ 0″	154	158	164	174	180	*

TABLE 2 — DESIRABLE WEIGHTS FOR MEN AND WOMEN

According to Height and Frame (Ages 25 and Over)

HEIGHT (In Shoes)	WEIGHT IN POUNDS (In Indoor Clothing)		
	SMALL FRAME	MEDIUM FRAME	LARGE FRAME
	MEN		
5' 2"	112-120	118-129	126-141
3"	115-123	121-133	129-144
4"	118-126	124-136	132-148
5"	121-129	127-139	135-152
6"	124-133	130-143	138-156
7"	128-137	134-147	142-161
8"	132-141	138-152	147-166
9"	136-145	142-156	151-170
10"	140-150	146-160	155-174
11"	144-154	150-165	159-179
6' 0"	148-158	154-170	164-184
1"	152-162	158-175	168-189
2"	156-167	162-180	173-194
3"	160-171	167-185	178-199
4"	164-175	172-190	182-204
	WOMEN		
4' 10"	92- 98	96-107	104-119
11"	94-101	98-110	106-122
5' 0"	96-104	101-113	109-125
1"	99-107	104-116	112-128
2"	102-110	107-119	115-131
3"	105-113	110-122	118-134
4"	108-116	113-126	121-138
5"	111-119	116-130	125-142
6"	114-123	120-135	129-146
7"	118-127	124-139	133-150
8"	122-131	128-143	137-154
9"	126-135	132-147	141-158
10"	130-140	136-151	145-163
11"	134-144	140-155	149-168
6' 0"	138-148	144-159	153-173

Metropolitan Life Insurance Company Statistical Bulletin — November-December 1959.

ALGAE — as used in medicines, these are single celled water plants including seaweed.

ALLERGIC — the state of sensitivity to a substance.

AMINO ACIDS — organic compounds forming the chief structure of proteins.

ANEMIA — a condition in which the blood is deficient either in quantity or in quality.

ANOMALY — any deviation from the normal.

ANOREXIA NERVOSA — a nervous condition with loss of appetite and severe loss of weight.

ANTIBIOTIC — a clinical substance produced by minute organisms and capable of destroying other minute living organisms.

ARTERIOSCLEROSIS — loss of elasticity, hardening and thickening of arteries.

ARTHRITIS — inflammation of a joint.

ATHEROSCLEROSIS — a condition of large and medium-sized arteries characterized by fatty degeneration or thickening of walls.

BACTERIA — minute living organisms which are concerned with fermentation and putrefaction.

CALORIE — (standard) the amount of heat necessary to raise one kilogram of water from zero to 1° centigrade.

CAPILLARIES — minute blood vessels which connect the small arteries and veins.

CARBOHYDRATE — a food including starches, sugars, celluloses and gums.

CARDIOVASCULAR — pertaining to the heart and blood vessels.

CARIES — decay or disintegration of bone or the calcified tissues of the teeth.

CARTILAGE — the gristle or elastic substance attached to joints and certain parts of the skeleton.

CEREBRAL — pertaining to the main portion of the brain.

CHEMICAL BALANCE — a normal ratio between the acid and base elements of the blood and body fluids.

CHOLESTEROL — a fatlike pearly substance found in animal fats and oils.

DIGESTION — the process of changing foods into a condition to be absorbed and used by the body.

ELECTROCARDIOGRAM — a graphic tracing of the electric current produced by the contraction of heart muscle.

ENDOCRINE — applied especially to glands which secrete internally, that is directly, into the blood or lymph.

ENZYME — an organic compound which accelerates or produces chemical reaction.

FETUS — the name given to the unborn offspring in the womb usually after the third month of pregnancy to the moment of birth.

GASTRIC JUICE — stomach contents which aid digestion.

GENE — a unit of heredity for a particular characteristic.

GENETIC — pertaining to birth or origin, inherited.

GRAM — a unit of weight in metric system equal to fifteen (15) grains.

HORMONE — a chemical substance formed in one organ and carried in the blood to other organs which it stimulates to activity.

INSULIN — a chemical substance formed in the pancreas and passed into the blood where it regulates the sugar metabolism.

INTRINSIC FACTOR — a chemical substance of the stomach necessary for the proper blood formation.

LACTATION — the period of secretion of milk or the total time of breast feeding.

LETHARGY—a state of drowsiness or inaction.

LYMPH—a transparent slightly yellow liquid found in the lymphatic vessels.

MALNUTRITION—any disorder of nutrition.

METABOLISM — the sum of all the chemical and physical processes by which life is produced and maintained.

MILLIGRAM — one-thousandth of a gram.

MINERAL — a nonorganic substance.

MUSCULAR DYSTROPHY — Faulty nutrition of muscle resulting in wasting of muscle tissue.

NEUROSIS — an emotional illness in which the personality remains more or less intact.

NUTRIENT — a substance carrying nourishment which affects the metabolic processes of the body.

OBESITY — an excessive accumulation of fat in the body.

OVERWEIGHT — excessive body weight above the normal.

PACIFIER — an oral device for sucking utilized to quiet infants.

PERNICIOUS ANEMIA — a form of anemia in which there is a defect in blood formation with great reduction in red blood cells which are deformed and abnormally large.

PHARYNX — the part of the throat between the mouth, back of the nose and the swallowing tube (esophagus).

PLACENTA — a cakelike mass which connects the fetus to womb.

PROTEIN — a food consisting mainly of amino acids.

PROTHROMBIN — a substance in the blood necessary for clotting.

RESPIRATORY — pertaining to the function of breathing.

RICKETS — a condition of abnormal bone formation in infants and children caused by a deficiency of vitamin D.

SATURATED FATS — solid or semi-solid fats produced by adding hydrogen.

SCURVY — a condition due to a deficiency of vitamin C and marked by bleeding gums, hemorrhages and anemia.

SIMMONDS DISEASE — a condition caused by wasting away of the master gland of the body (pituitary) and resulting in premature aging, severe weight loss and mental symptoms.

SOLUBLE — able to be dissolved.

TRAUMA — a wound, injury.

TRIMESTER — a period of three months.

TRYPTOPHAN — an amino acid.

UNSATURATED FATS — liquid fats (oils) not containing excessive hydrogen.

VASCULAR — pertaining to or containing blood vessels.

VITAMIN — organic substance found in small amounts in many foods and necessary for normal metabolic functioning of the body.

PUBLICATIONS RECOMMENDED FOR DISTRIBUTION TO DIABETICS:

1. MEAL PLANNING: Prepared by Committees of American Diabetic Association and The American Dietetic Association in cooperation with Chronic Disease Program, Public Health Service, Department of Health, Education and Welfare.

Copies may be purchased from The American Dietetic Association, 620 North Michigan Avenue, Chicago 11, Illinois.

2. TAKING CARE OF DIABETES: Public Health Service Publication No. 567. Copies may be purchased from Supt. of Documents, U. S. Government Printing Office, Washington 25, D. C.

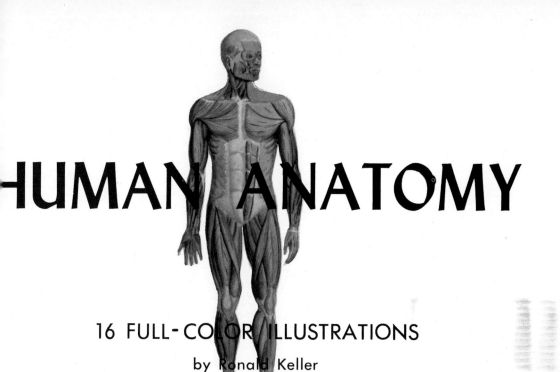

HUMAN ANATOMY

16 FULL-COLOR ILLUSTRATIONS
by Ronald Keller

Prepared in consultation with

Charles N. Berry, Ph.D.

Seton Hall College of Medicine and Dentistry

Table of Contents

By

C. S. HAMMOND and COMPANY

S. Hammond & Co., N. Y.

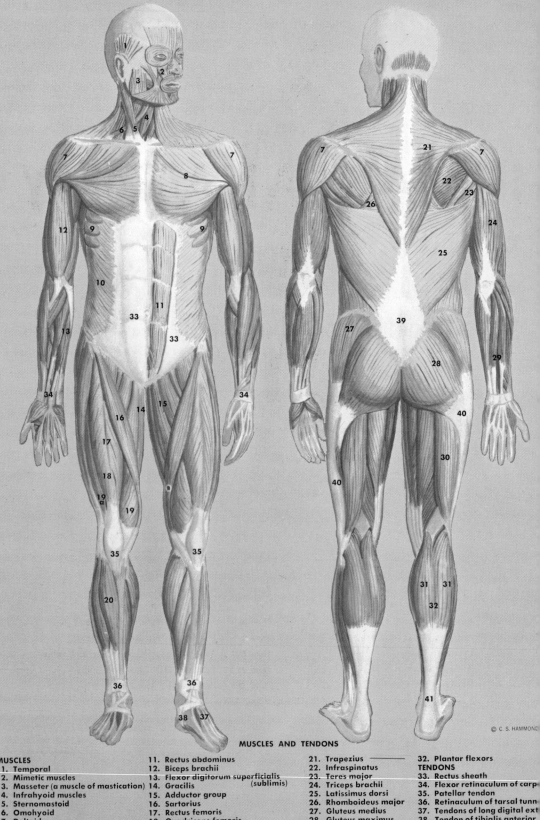

MUSCLES AND TENDONS

© C. S. HAMMOND

MUSCLES
1. Temporal
2. Mimetic muscles
3. Masseter (a muscle of mastication)
4. Infrahyoid muscles
5. Sternomastoid
6. Omohyoid
7. Deltoid
8. Pectoral muscles
9. Serratus anterior
10. External oblique

11. Rectus abdominus
12. Biceps brachii
13. Flexor digitorum superficialis
    (sublimis)
14. Gracilis
15. Adductor group
16. Sartorius
17. Rectus femoris
18. Quadriceps femoris
19. Vastus medialis
19a. Vastus lateralis
20. Dorsiflexors

21. Trapezius ———
22. Infraspinatus
23. Teres major
24. Triceps brachii
25. Latissimus dorsi
26. Rhomboideus major
27. Gluteus medius
28. Gluteus maximus
29. Digital extensors
30. Hamstring muscles
31. Gastrocnemius

32. Plantar flexors
TENDONS
33. Rectus sheath
34. Flexor retinaculum of carp
35. Patellar tendon
36. Retinaculum of tarsal tunn
37. Tendons of long digital ext
38. Tendon of tibialis anterior
39. Lumbodorsal fascia
40. Fascia lata
41. Achilles

Plate

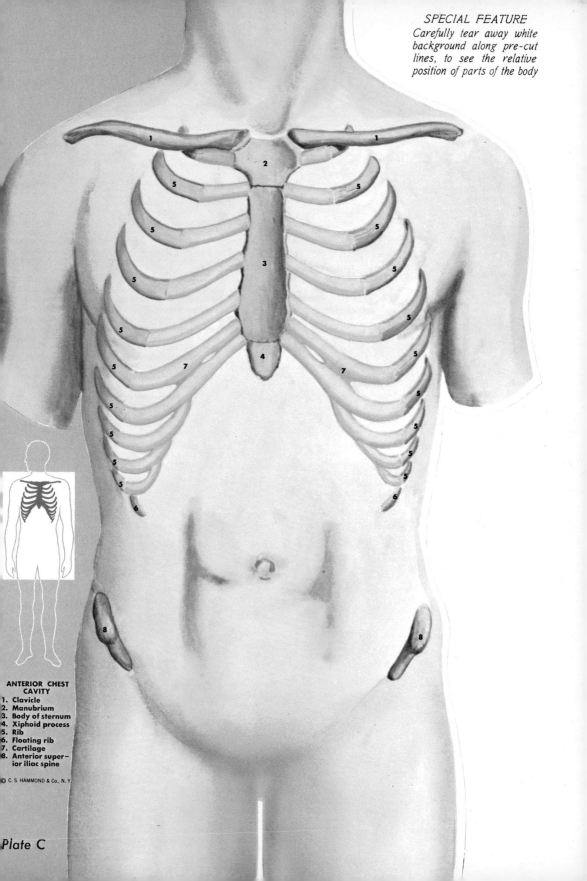

SPECIAL FEATURE
*Carefully tear away white
background along pre-cut
lines, to see the relative
position of parts of the body*

**ANTERIOR CHEST
CAVITY**
1. Clavicle
2. Manubrium
3. Body of sternum
4. Xiphoid process
5. Rib
6. Floating rib
7. Cartilage
8. Anterior super-
   ior iliac spine

© C. S. HAMMOND & Co., N. Y.

Plate C

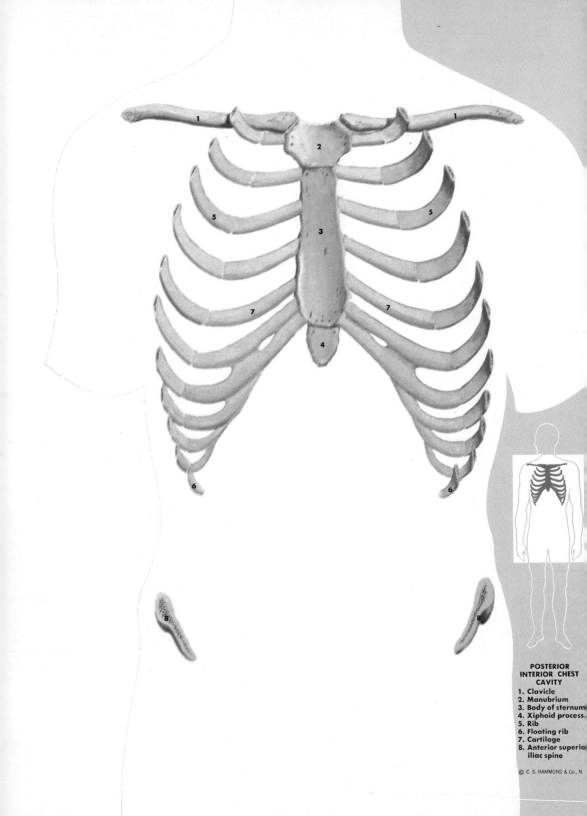

POSTERIOR INTERIOR CHEST CAVITY

1. Clavicle
2. Manubrium
3. Body of sternum
4. Xiphoid process
5. Rib
6. Floating rib
7. Cartilage
8. Anterior superior iliac spine

© C. S. HAMMOND & Co., N.

Plate D

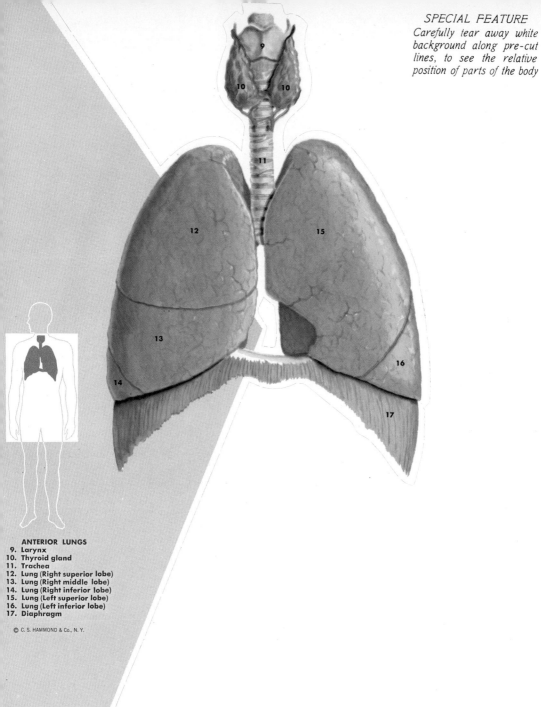

ANTERIOR LUNGS
9. Larynx
10. Thyroid gland
11. Trachea
12. Lung (Right superior lobe)
13. Lung (Right middle lobe)
14. Lung (Right inferior lobe)
15. Lung (Left superior lobe)
16. Lung (Left inferior lobe)
17. Diaphragm

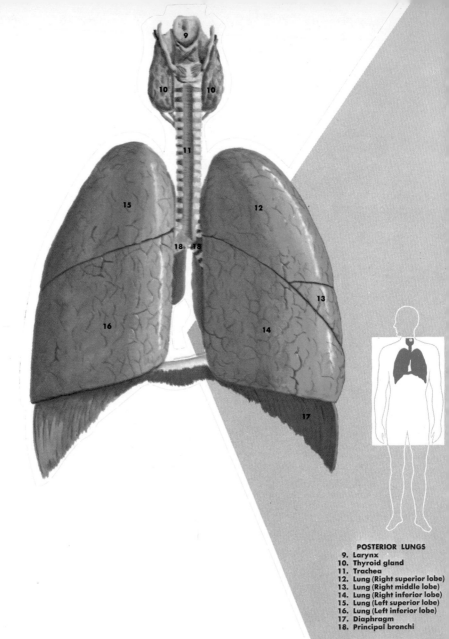

POSTERIOR LUNGS
9. Larynx
10. Thyroid gland
11. Trachea
12. Lung (Right superior lobe)
13. Lung (Right middle lobe)
14. Lung (Right inferior lobe)
15. Lung (Left superior lobe)
16. Lung (Left inferior lobe)
17. Diaphragm
18. Principal bronchi

Plate F

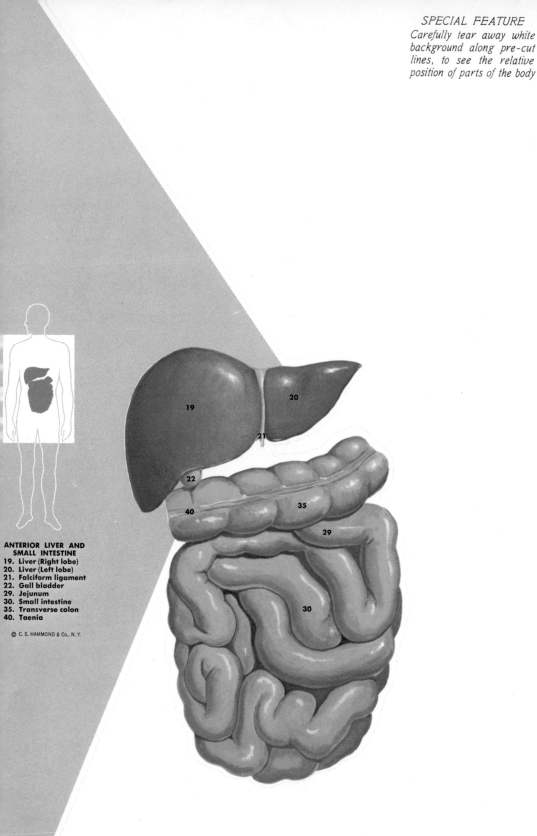

SPECIAL FEATURE
Carefully tear away white
background along pre-cut
lines, to see the relative
position of parts of the body

**ANTERIOR LIVER AND
SMALL INTESTINE**
19. Liver (Right lobe)
20. Liver (Left lobe)
21. Falciform ligament
22. Gall bladder
29. Jejunum
30. Small intestine
35. Transverse colon
40. Taenia

© C. S. HAMMOND & Co., N. Y.

Plate G

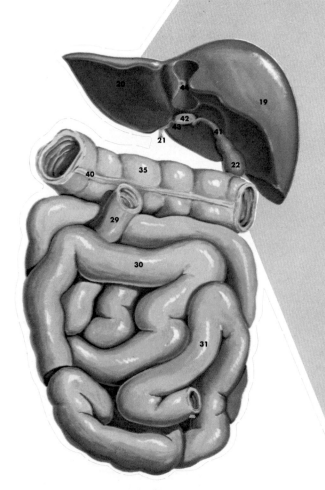

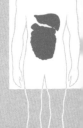

POSTERIOR LIVER AND SMALL INTESTINE

19. Liver (Right lobe)
20. Liver (Left lobe)
21. Falciform ligament
22. Gall bladder
29. Jejunum
30. Small intestine
31. Ileum
35. Transverse colon
40. Taenia coli
41. Cystic duct
42. Portal vein
43. Hepatic artery
44. Hepatic vein

© C. S. HAMMOND & Co., N. Y.

Plate H

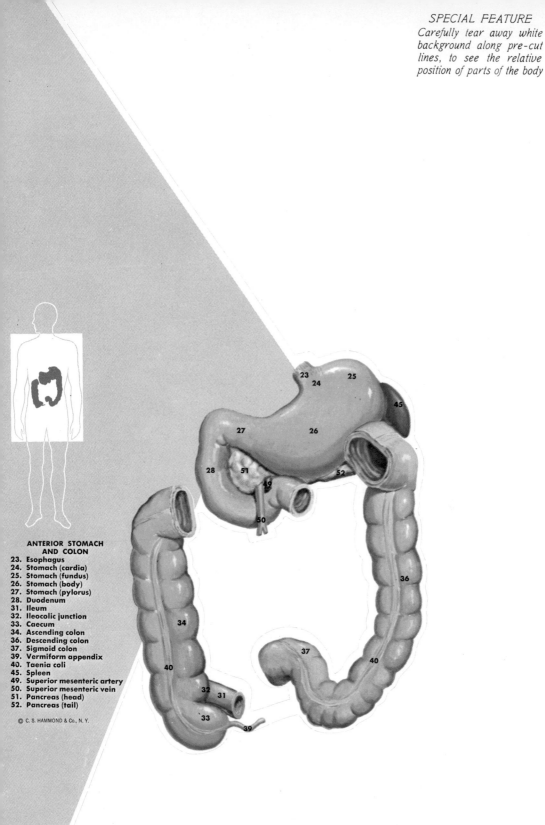

**ANTERIOR STOMACH
AND COLON**
23. Esophagus
24. Stomach (cardia)
25. Stomach (fundus)
26. Stomach (body)
27. Stomach (pylorus)
28. Duodenum
31. Ileum
32. Ileocolic junction
33. Caecum
34. Ascending colon
36. Descending colon
37. Sigmoid colon
39. Vermiform appendix
40. Taenia coli
45. Spleen
49. Superior mesenteric artery
50. Superior mesenteric vein
51. Pancreas (head)
52. Pancreas (tail)

© C. S. HAMMOND & Co., N. Y.

Plate 1

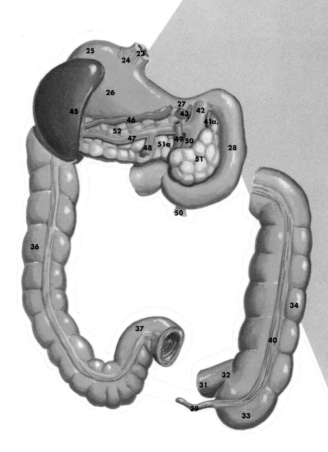
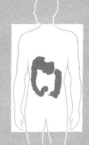

**POSTERIOR STOMACH
AND COLON**

23. Esophagus
24. Stomach (cardia)
25. Stomach (fundus)
26. Stomach (body)
27. Stomach (pylorus)
28. Duodenum
31. Ileum
32. Ileocolic junction
33. Caecum
34. Ascending colon
36. Descending colon
37. Sigmoid colon
39. Vermiform appendix
40. Taenia coli
41a. Common bile duct
42. Portal vein
43. Hepatic artery
45. Spleen
46. Splenic artery
47. Splenic vein
48. Inferior mesenteric
    vein
49. Superior mesenteric
    artery
50. Superior mesenteric
    vein
51. Pancreas (head)
51a. Pancreas (body)
52. Pancreas (tail)

Plate J

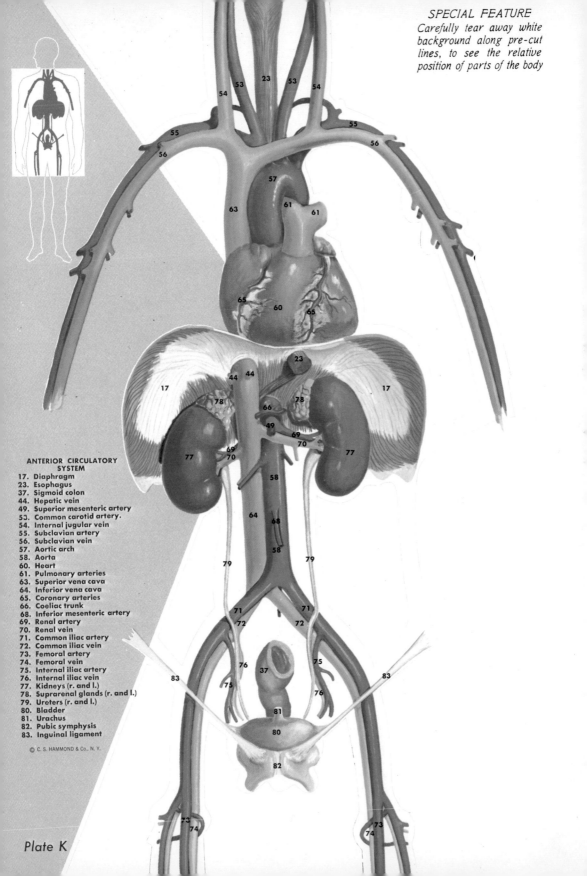

SPECIAL FEATURE
Carefully tear away white background along pre-cut lines, to see the relative position of parts of the body

ANTERIOR CIRCULATORY SYSTEM
17. Diaphragm
23. Esophagus
37. Sigmoid colon
44. Hepatic vein
49. Superior mesenteric artery
53. Common carotid artery.
54. Internal jugular vein
55. Subclavian artery
56. Subclavian vein
57. Aortic arch
58. Aorta
60. Heart
61. Pulmonary arteries
63. Superior vena cava
64. Inferior vena cava
65. Coronary arteries
66. Coeliac trunk
68. Inferior mesenteric artery
69. Renal artery
70. Renal vein
71. Common iliac artery
72. Common iliac vein
73. Femoral artery
74. Femoral vein
75. Internal iliac artery
76. Internal iliac vein
77. Kidneys (r. and l.)
78. Suprarenal glands (r. and l.)
79. Ureters (r. and l.)
80. Bladder
81. Urachus
82. Pubic symphysis
83. Inguinal ligament

© C. S. HAMMOND & Co., N. Y.

Plate K

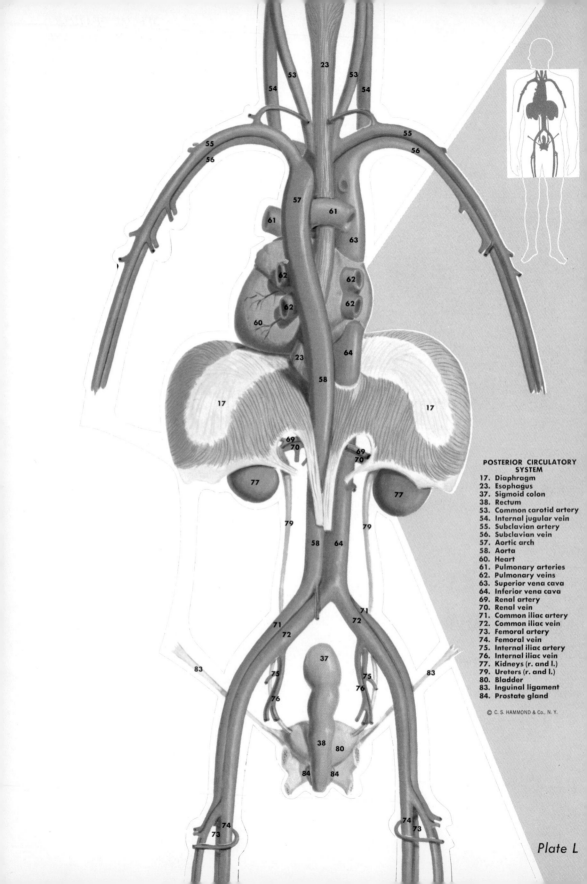

POSTERIOR CIRCULATORY SYSTEM

17. Diaphragm
23. Esophagus
37. Sigmoid colon
38. Rectum
53. Common carotid artery
54. Internal jugular vein
55. Subclavian artery
56. Subclavian vein
57. Aortic arch
58. Aorta
60. Heart
61. Pulmonary arteries
62. Pulmonary veins
63. Superior vena cava
64. Inferior vena cava
69. Renal artery
70. Renal vein
71. Common iliac artery
72. Common iliac vein
73. Femoral artery
74. Femoral vein
75. Internal iliac artery
76. Internal iliac vein
77. Kidneys (r. and l.)
79. Ureters (r. and l.)
80. Bladder
83. Inguinal ligament
84. Prostate gland

© C. S. HAMMOND & Co., N. Y.

Plate L

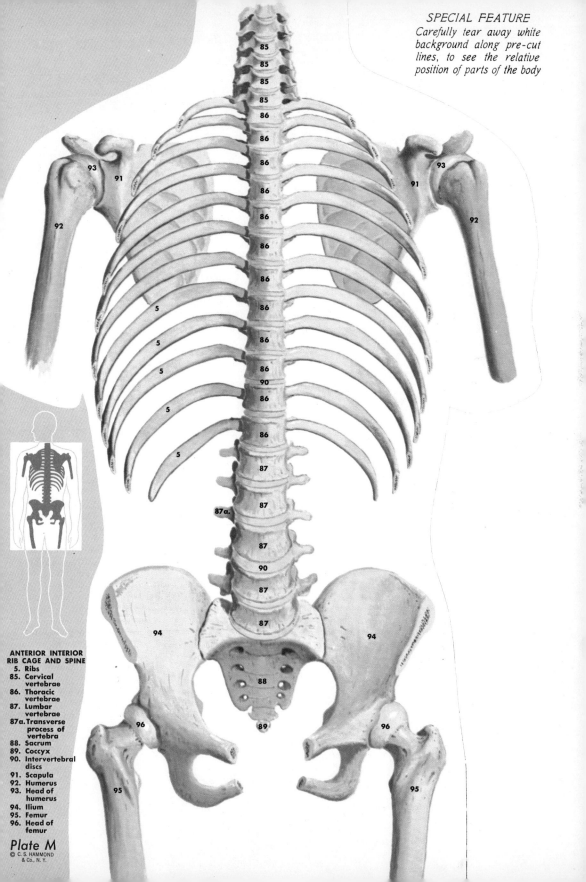

SPECIAL FEATURE
Carefully tear away white
background along pre-cut
lines, to see the relative
position of parts of the body

**ANTERIOR INTERIOR
RIB CAGE AND SPINE**
5. Ribs
85. Cervical
   vertebrae
86. Thoracic
   vertebrae
87. Lumbar
   vertebrae
87a. Transverse
   process of
   vertebra
88. Sacrum
89. Coccyx
90. Intervertebral
   discs
91. Scapula
92. Humerus
93. Head of
   humerus
94. Ilium
95. Femur
96. Head of
   femur

Plate M
© C. S. HAMMOND
& Co., N. Y.

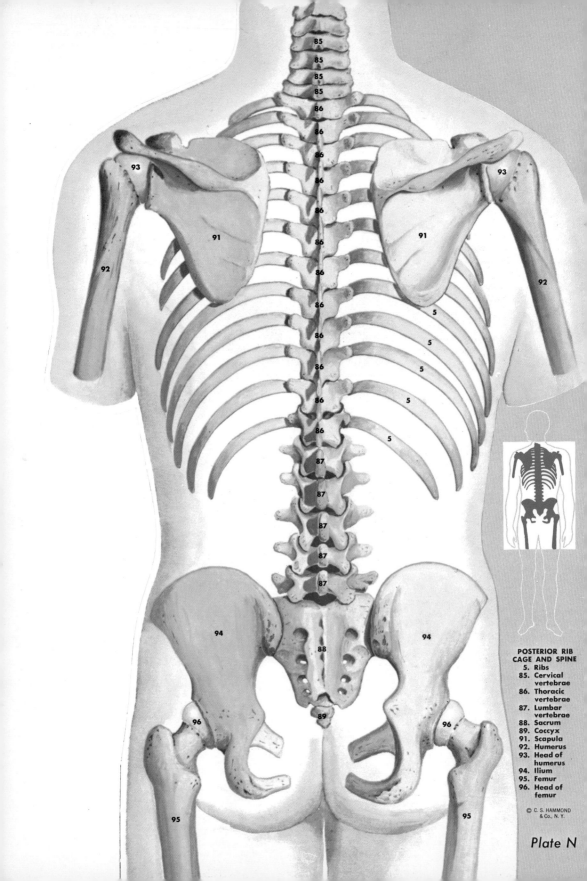

POSTERIOR RIB
CAGE AND SPINE
  5. Ribs
 85. Cervical
     vertebrae
 86. Thoracic
     vertebrae
 87. Lumbar
     vertebrae
 88. Sacrum
 89. Coccyx
 91. Scapula
 92. Humerus
 93. Head of
     humerus
 94. Ilium
 95. Femur
 96. Head of
     femur

© C. S. HAMMOND
  & Co., N. Y.

Plate N

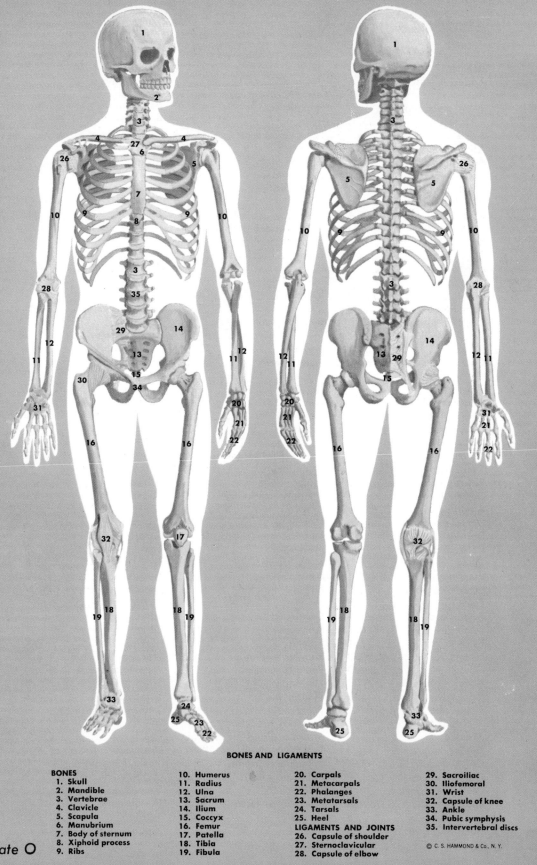

BONES AND LIGAMENTS

BONES
1. Skull
2. Mandible
3. Vertebrae
4. Clavicle
5. Scapula
6. Manubrium
7. Body of sternum
8. Xiphoid process
9. Ribs

10. Humerus
11. Radius
12. Ulna
13. Sacrum
14. Ilium
15. Coccyx
16. Femur
17. Patella
18. Tibia
19. Fibula

20. Carpals
21. Metacarpals
22. Phalanges
23. Metatarsals
24. Tarsals
25. Heel

LIGAMENTS AND JOINTS
26. Capsule of shoulder
27. Sternoclavicular
28. Capsule of elbow

29. Sacroiliac
30. Iliofemoral
31. Wrist
32. Capsule of knee
33. Ankle
34. Pubic symphysis
35. Intervertebral discs

© C. S. HAMMOND & Co., N. Y.

GLOSSARY and INDEX

Plate P

HUMAN ANATOMY

the Female

20 FULL-COLOR ILLUSTRATIONS
by Ronald Keller

Prepared in consultation with

Christian A. Hovde, Ph. D.,

Department of Anatomy

Seton Hall College of Medicine and Dentistry

Table of Contents

THE STUDY OF ANATOMY

The word ANATOMY is derived from two Greek words which mean, literally, "to cut apart". Through usage it has come to mean "an analysis of the structure of things".

It is hardly necessary to mention the great benefit that has come to Mankind from the study of anatomy in medical schools and research centers. That is, of course, the study which has been engaged in by professionals and experts.

Most of us, obviously, cannot be experts. The study of anatomy is really not essential to our well-being. Our wonderful bodies develop, grow, and keep themselves in repair with very little conscious aid from their owners. Whether we know how to spell EPIGLOTTIS or know where it is or what it looks like, this little part of each of us is constantly at its job, which is to guard the entrance of the TRACHEA so that the food we swallow is directed to the ESOPHAGUS and does not drop into the BRONCHI. And so it is with our HEART, LIVER, GALL BLADDER, etc. They do their work and are seldom heard from unless illness or an accident intervenes. If this happens we must consult a physician who has spent many years in the study of human anatomy.

Actually the body is so complex that very few individuals, even physicians, have a thorough knowledge of every part of it. But, it is possible for everyone to have a general knowledge of his physical make-up. This knowledge will result in a better understanding of how to care for your body and a better understanding of your doctor's advice when you must consult him.

We may hear and even use such terms as SACRO-ILIAC or THYROID and yet have only a hazy notion of what these terms mean.

How much easier it is for your doctor to explain your physical self to you if you understand the terms he uses and if you have a rudimentary understanding of the areas being discussed.

Even in this short introduction it has been quite necessary to use anatomical terms. However, right here we have the means in the following pages to associate these terms with pictures of the parts they represent and to learn their locations and their relation to other parts.

This booklet does not tell "how" the body and its parts function—that would be the subject of physiology—but it does tell, without going into exhaustive detail, "what" its components are and gives in pictures and words a map of the territory within you.

Printed in U.

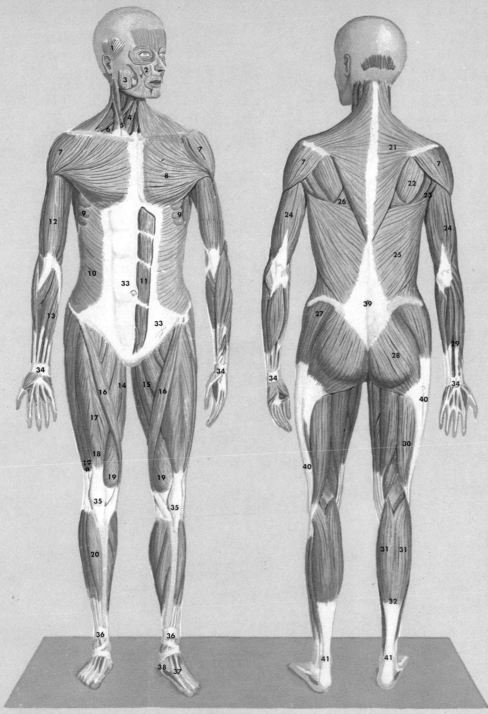

MUSCLES AND TENDONS

MUSCLES
1. Temporal
2. Mimetic muscles
3. Masseter (a muscle of mastication)
4. Infrahyoid muscles
5. Sternomastoid
6. Omohyoid
7. Deltoid
8. Pectoral muscles
9. Serratus anterior
10. External oblique
11. Rectus abdominus
12. Biceps brachii
13. Flexor digitorum superficialis (sublimis)
14. Gracilis

15. Adductor group
16. Sartorius
17. Rectus femoris
18. Quadriceps femoris
19. Vastus medialis
19a. Vastus lateralis
20. Dorsiflexors
21. Trapezius
22. Infraspinatus
23. Teres major
24. Triceps brachii
25. Latissimus dorsi
26. Rhomboideus major
27. Gluteus medius
28. Gluteus maximus

29. Digital extensors
30. Hamstring muscles
31. Gastrocnemius
32. Plantar flexors
TENDONS
33. Rectus sheath
34. Flexor retinaculum of carpal tunnel
35. Patellar tendon
36. Retinaculum of tarsal tunnel
37. Tendons of long digital extensors
38. Tendon of tibialis anterior
39. Lumbodorsal fascia
40. Fascia lata
41. Achilles

© C. S. HAMMOND & Co., N. Y.

1

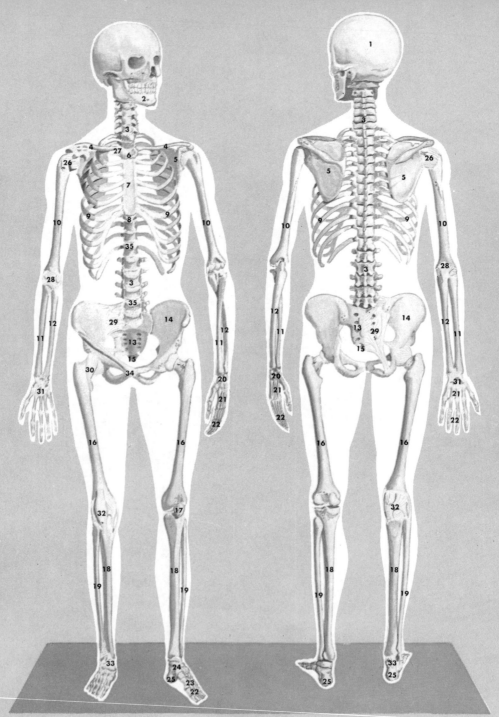

BONES
1. Skull
2. Mandible
3. Vertebrae
4. Clavicle
5. Scapula
6. Manubrium
7. Body of sternum
8. Xiphoid process
9. Ribs
10. Humerus
11. Radius
12. Ulna

BONES AND LIGAMENTS
13. Sacrum
14. Ilium
15. Coccyx
16. Femur
17. Patella
18. Tibia
19. Fibula
20. Carpals
21. Metacarpals
22. Phalanges
23. Metatarsals
24. Tarsals
25. Heel

LIGAMENTS AND JOINTS
26. Capsule of shoulder
27. Sternoclavicular
28. Capsule of elbow
29. Sacroiliac
30. Iliofemoral
31. Wrist
32. Capsule of knee
33. Ankle
34. Pubic symphysis
35. Intervertebral discs

© C. S. HAMMOND & Co., N. Y.

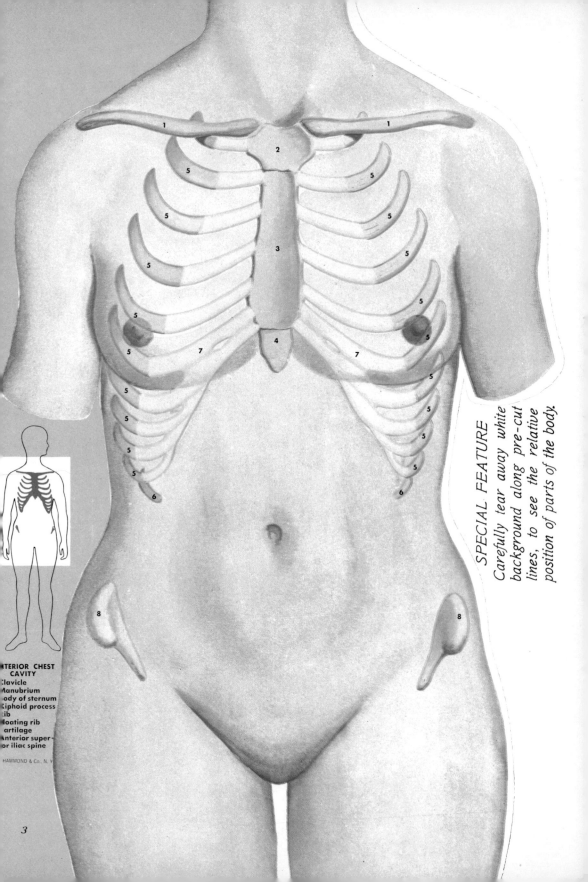

ANTERIOR CHEST
CAVITY

Clavicle
Manubrium
Body of sternum
Xiphoid process
Rib
Floating rib
Cartilage
Anterior super-
ior iliac spine

SPECIAL FEATURE
Carefully tear away white background along pre-cut lines, to see the relative position of parts of the body.

3

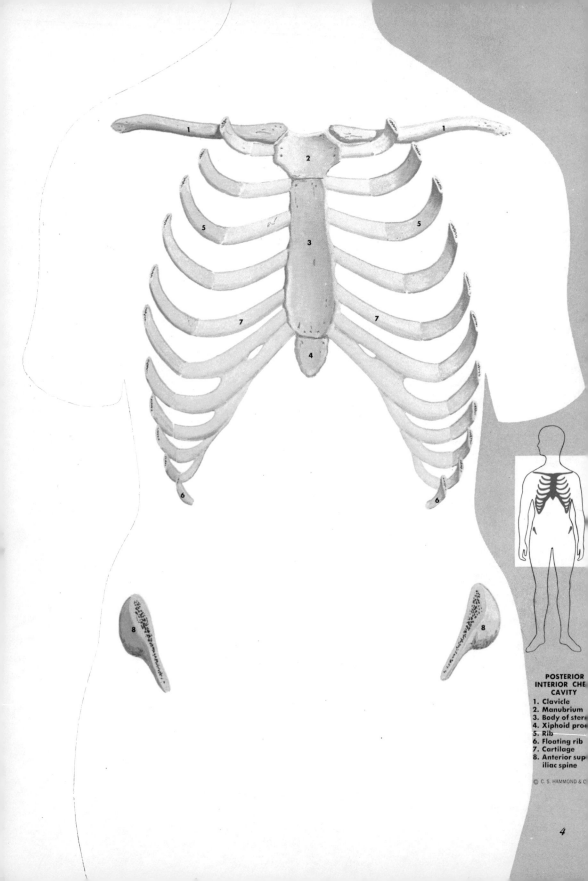

POSTERIOR
INTERIOR CHE
CAVITY

1. Clavicle
2. Manubrium
3. Body of stern
4. Xiphoid proc
5. Rib
6. Floating rib
7. Cartilage
8. Anterior sup
iliac spine

© C. S. HAMMOND & C

4

SPECIAL FEATURE
Carefully tear away white
background along pre-cut
lines, to see the relative
position of parts of the body.

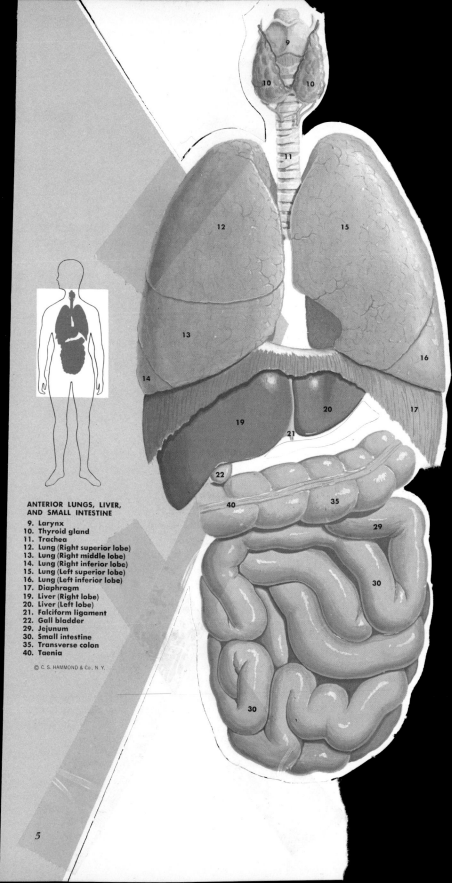

**ANTERIOR LUNGS, LIVER,
AND SMALL INTESTINE**

9. Larynx
10. Thyroid gland
11. Trachea
12. Lung (Right superior lobe)
13. Lung (Right middle lobe)
14. Lung (Right inferior lobe)
15. Lung (Left superior lobe)
16. Lung (Left inferior lobe)
17. Diaphragm
19. Liver (Right lobe)
20. Liver (Left lobe)
21. Falciform ligament
22. Gall bladder
29. Jejunum
30. Small intestine
35. Transverse colon
40. Taenia

5

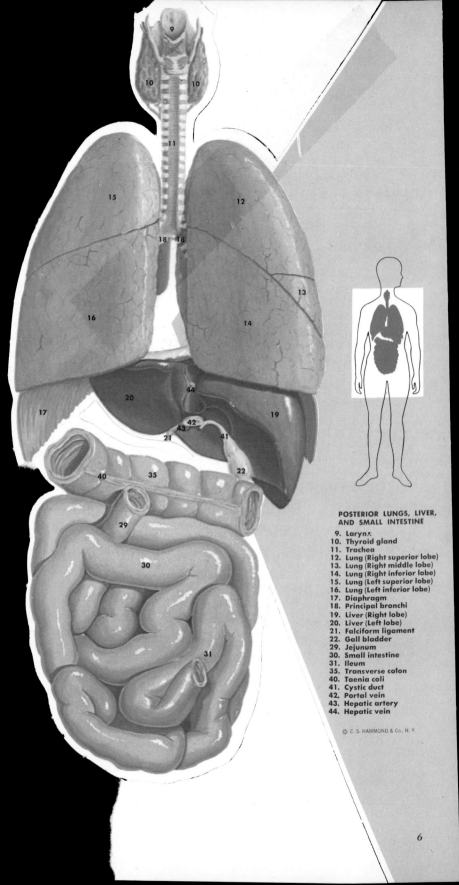

POSTERIOR LUNGS, LIVER, AND SMALL INTESTINE

9. Larynx
10. Thyroid gland
11. Trachea
12. Lung (Right superior lobe)
13. Lung (Right middle lobe)
14. Lung (Right inferior lobe)
15. Lung (Left superior lobe)
16. Lung (Left inferior lobe)
17. Diaphragm
18. Principal bronchi
19. Liver (Right lobe)
20. Liver (Left lobe)
21. Falciform ligament
22. Gall bladder
29. Jejunum
30. Small intestine
31. Ileum
35. Transverse colon
40. Taenia coli
41. Cystic duct
42. Portal vein
43. Hepatic artery
44. Hepatic vein

SPECIAL FEATURE

Carefully tear away white background along pre-cut lines, to see the relative position of parts of the body.

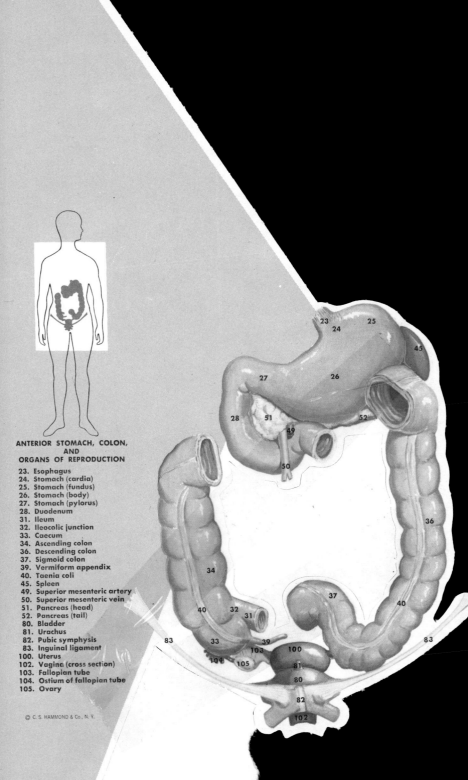

ANTERIOR STOMACH, COLON, AND ORGANS OF REPRODUCTION

23. Esophagus
24. Stomach (cardia)
25. Stomach (fundus)
26. Stomach (body)
27. Stomach (pylorus)
28. Duodenum
31. Ileum
32. Ileocolic junction
33. Caecum
34. Ascending colon
36. Descending colon
37. Sigmoid colon
39. Vermiform appendix
40. Taenia coli
45. Spleen
49. Superior mesenteric artery
50. Superior mesenteric vein
51. Pancreas (head)
52. Pancreas (tail)
80. Bladder
81. Urachus
82. Pubic symphysis
83. Inguinal ligament
100. Uterus
102. Vagina (cross section)
103. Fallopian tube
104. Ostium of fallopian tube
105. Ovary

7

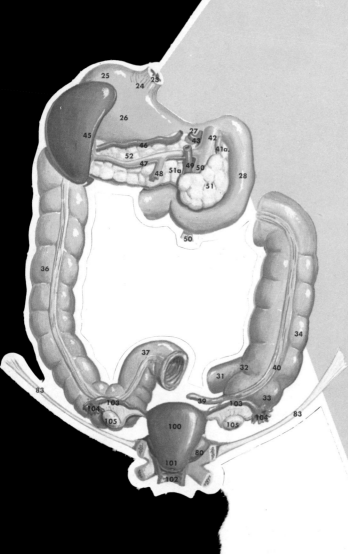

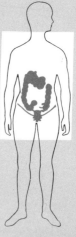

POSTERIOR STOMACH, COLO
AND
ORGANS OF REPRODUCTIO

23. Esophagus
24. Stomach (cardia)
25. Stomach (fundus)
26. Stomach (body)
27. Stomach (pylorus)
28. Duodenum
31. Ileum
32. Ileocolic junction
33. Caecum
34. Ascending colon
36. Descending colon
37. Sigmoid colon
39. Vermiform appendix
40. Taenia coli
41a. Common bile duct
42. Portal vein
43. Hepatic artery
45. Spleen
46. Splenic artery
47. Splenic vein
48. Inferior mesenteric vein
49. Superior mesenteric arter
50. Superior mesenteric vein
51. Pancreas (head)
51a. Pancreas (body)
52. Pancreas (tail)
80. Bladder
83. Inguinal ligament
100. Uterus
101. Cervix
102. Vagina (cross section)
103. Fallopian tube
104. Ostium of fallopian tube
105. Ovary

8

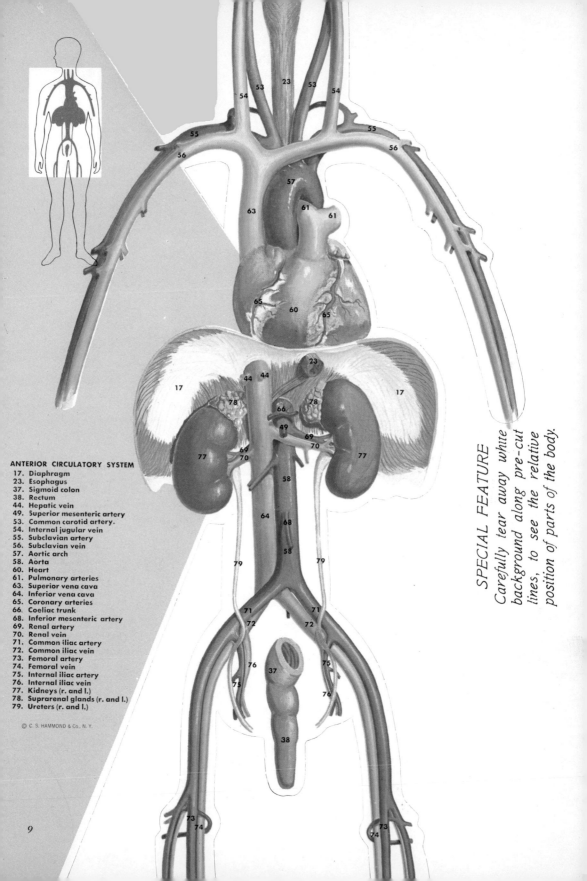

ANTERIOR CIRCULATORY SYSTEM

17. Diaphragm
23. Esophagus
37. Sigmoid colon
38. Rectum
44. Hepatic vein
49. Superior mesenteric artery
53. Common carotid artery.
54. Internal jugular vein
55. Subclavian artery
56. Subclavian vein
57. Aortic arch
58. Aorta
60. Heart
61. Pulmonary arteries
63. Superior vena cava
64. Inferior vena cava
65. Coronary arteries
66. Coeliac trunk
68. Inferior mesenteric artery
69. Renal artery
70. Renal vein
71. Common iliac artery
72. Common iliac vein
73. Femoral artery
74. Femoral vein
75. Internal iliac artery
76. Internal iliac vein
77. Kidneys (r. and l.)
78. Suprarenal glands (r. and l.)
79. Ureters (r. and l.)

© C. S. HAMMOND & Co., N. Y.

SPECIAL FEATURE
Carefully tear away white
background along pre-cut
lines, to see the relative
position of parts of the body.

9

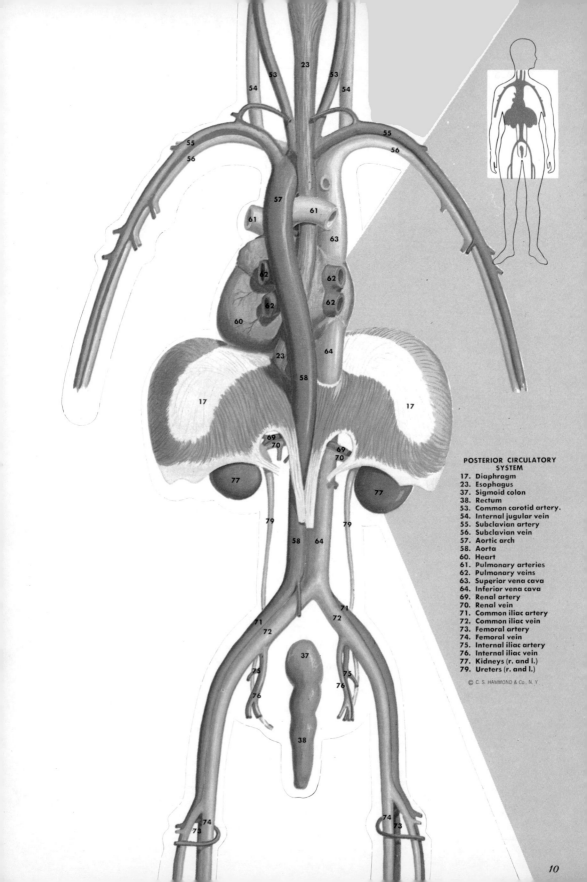

POSTERIOR CIRCULATORY SYSTEM

17. Diaphragm
23. Esophagus
37. Sigmoid colon
38. Rectum
53. Common carotid artery.
54. Internal jugular vein
55. Subclavian artery
56. Subclavian vein
57. Aortic arch
58. Aorta
60. Heart
61. Pulmonary arteries
62. Pulmonary veins
63. Superior vena cava
64. Inferior vena cava
69. Renal artery
70. Renal vein
71. Common iliac artery
72. Common iliac vein
73. Femoral artery
74. Femoral vein
75. Internal iliac artery
76. Internal iliac vein
77. Kidneys (r. and l.)
79. Ureters (r. and l.)

© C. S. HAMMOND & Co., N. Y.

10

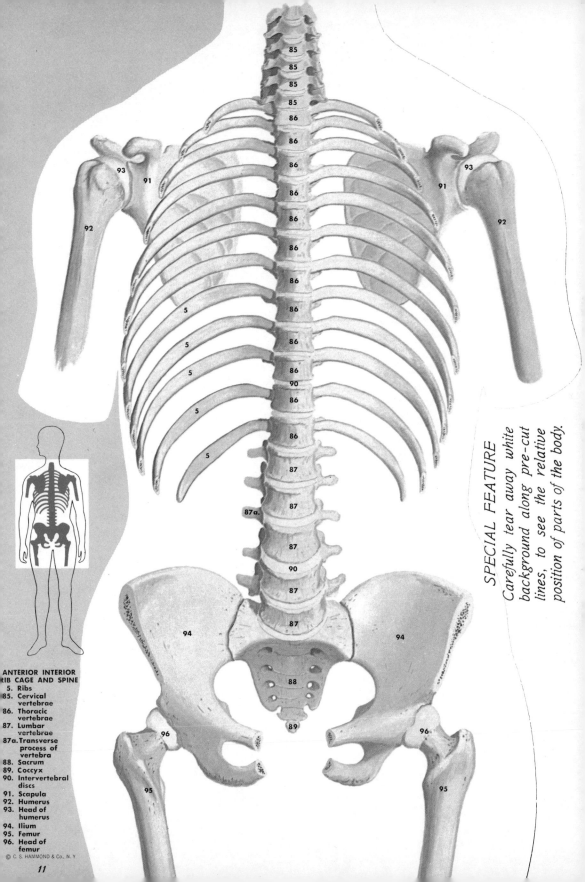

ANTERIOR INTERIOR
RIB CAGE AND SPINE
   5. Ribs
  85. Cervical
      vertebrae
  86. Thoracic
      vertebrae
  87. Lumbar
      vertebrae
 87a. Transverse
      process of
      vertebra
  88. Sacrum
  89. Coccyx
  90. Intervertebral
      discs
  91. Scapula
  92. Humerus
  93. Head of
      humerus
  94. Ilium
  95. Femur
  96. Head of
      femur

© C. S. HAMMOND & Co., N. Y.

SPECIAL FEATURE
Carefully tear away white
background along pre-cut
lines, to see the relative
position of parts of the body.

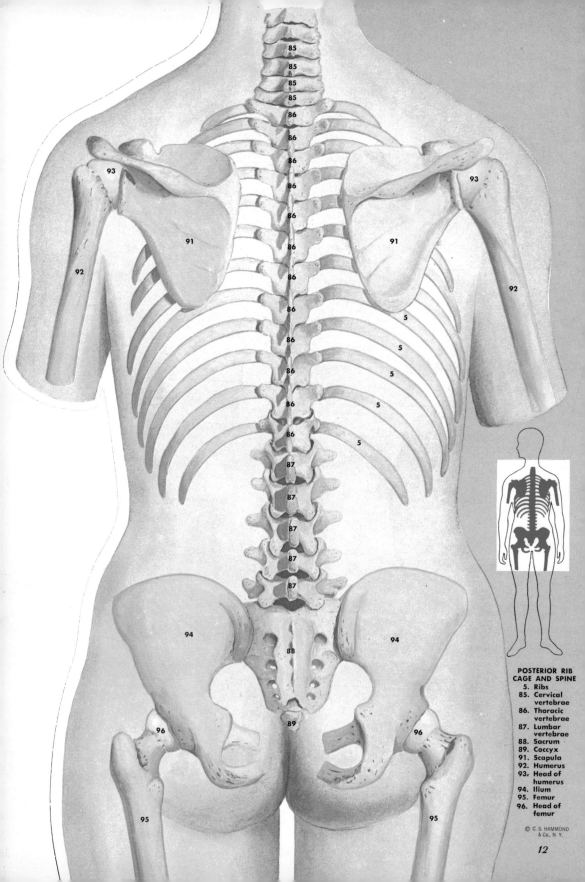

85
85
85
85
86
86
86
86
86
86
86
86
86
86
86
86
87
87
87
87
87
88
89

93 93
91 91
92 92
5
5
5
5
5
94 94
96 96
95 95

12

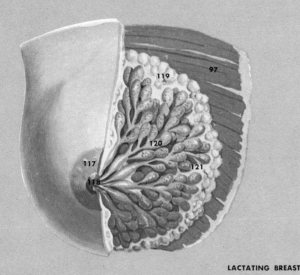

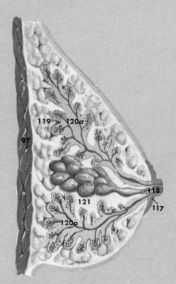

LACTATING BREAST

97. Pectoralis major muscle
117. Areola
118. Nipple
119. Fat
120. Lactiferous (milk producing) glands and ducts
120a. Cross section of gland and duct
121. Tissue separating and supporting glandular tissue

STRUCTURE OF THE MAMMARY GLANDS

The mammary glands are composed of three major elements:
1. Their skin covering and special structures (nipple, areola).
2. The lactiferous glands or functional units of the breast.
3. The supporting structures, the connective tissue "ligaments" and the fat tissue that makes up the mass of the breast.

The breast is supported by the "suspensory ligaments." These are anchored to the sheet of connective tissue surrounding the pectoralis major muscle, and extend in a complex network separated by the fat tissue outward to the skin. The lactiferous glands are buried in the supporting tissues and empty outward onto the surface of the nipple. These glands at first are very small and clustered just beneath the nipple and areola. In pregnancy they enlarge and push downward into the mass of the breast causing it to enlarge in turn. The enlargement continues through the period of breast feeding, following which the glands gradually grow smaller and the entire breast returns to normal size.

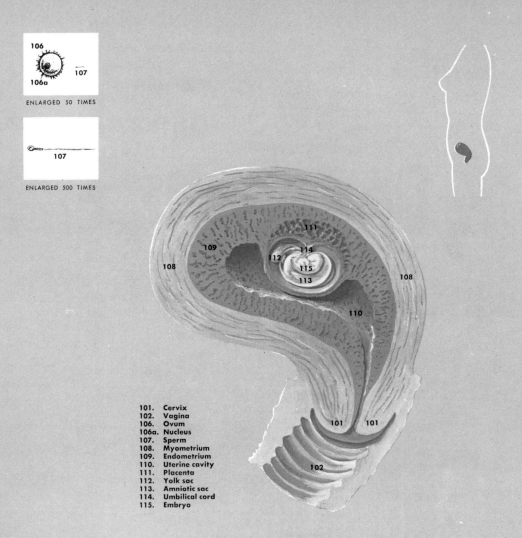

ENLARGED 50 TIMES

ENLARGED 500 TIMES

101. Cervix
102. Vagina
106. Ovum
106a. Nucleus
107. Sperm
108. Myometrium
109. Endometrium
110. Uterine cavity
111. Placenta
112. Yolk sac
113. Amniotic sac
114. Umbilical cord
115. Embryo

CROSS SECTION OF THE UTERUS

The female generative organs include the ovaries, the Fallopian Tubes, the uterus with its cervix or neck, and the vagina. The ovum leaves the ovary, passes into the Fallopian Tube, is fertilized, and development of the embryo begins as it passes into the uterine cavity. The uterus is composed of muscle wall (myometrium) lined by layers of cells and glands (endometrium). The fertilized egg attaches itself to the endometrium, and the walls of the egg and the endometrium, where they are in contact, thicken and interlace providing contact area (the placenta) between the mother and developing child. The umbilical cord connects the embryo with the placenta. The yolk sac is a separate development of the embryo, providing food materials until the placenta is established. It finally disappears.

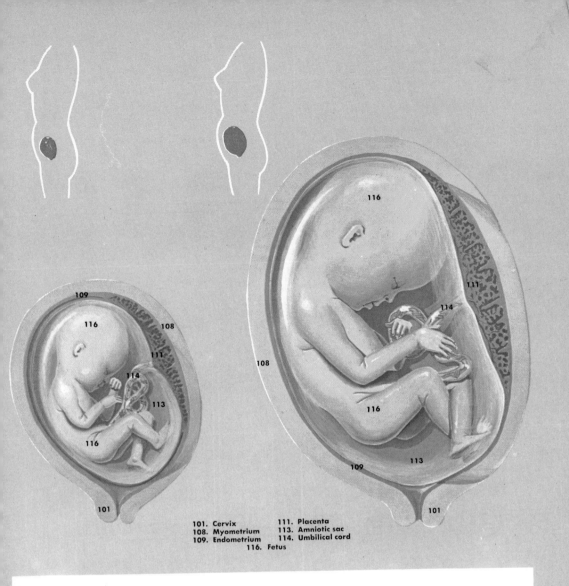

101. Cervix
108. Myometrium
109. Endometrium
116. Fetus
111. Placenta
113. Amniotic sac
114. Umbilical cord

THE FETUS AT 3 1/2 AND 6 MONTHS

Most of the definitive development of the fetus occurs during the first 3½ months, and the remaining 5½ months is primarily concerned with gradual increase in size and maturation of organs already begun. The fetus receives all of its nourishment through the placenta and umbilical cord. There is no direct contact between fetal and maternal blood in the placenta. During its entire development, the fetus floats in a fluid (amniotic fluid) contained within a sac (the amniotic sac) attached to the placenta. This sac is in turn surrounded by the uterine cavity, the endometrium and the muscle or myometrium of the uterus.

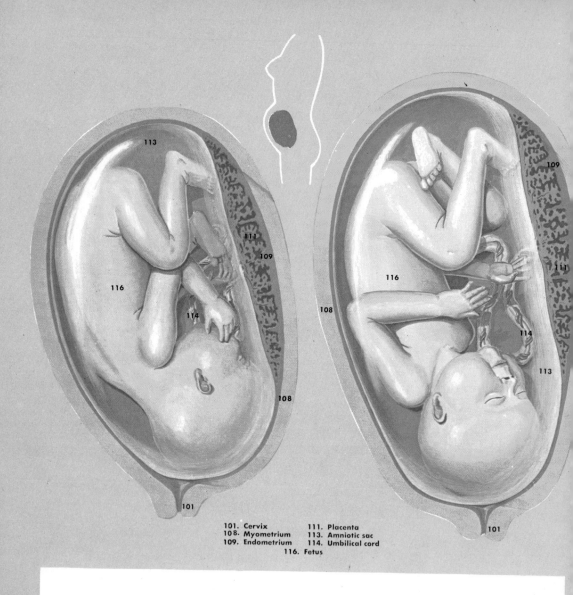

101. Cervix	111. Placenta
108. Myometrium	113. Amniotic sac
109. Endometrium	114. Umbilical cord
116. Fetus	

THE FETUS AT 8 AND 9 MONTHS

Until birth, the fetus is surrounded by the amniotic sac and fluid, and attached to the placenta by the umbilical cord. The fetus continues to increase in size and the uterus stretches to accommodate it. Usually before the eighth month the fetus assumes a head-downward position. At birth, the amniotic sac ruptures, the fluid escapes, and the child is slowly pushed out of the uterine cavity by the contractions of the myometrium. Shortly after birth of the child, the placenta is similarly expelled having been detached from the endometrium.

HEREDITY

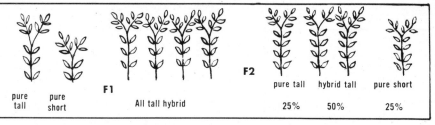

e of Mendel's experiments
th peas (made in the
idle of the 19th century).

pure tall | pure short | F1 — All tall hybrid | F2 — pure tall 25% | hybrid tall 50% | pure short 25%

In the hybrids (generation F1), the characteristic "shortness" goes into hiding (is recessive), "tallness" is dominant. In offspring of these hybrids (generation F2), pure tallness and pure shortness again appear in definite proportions.

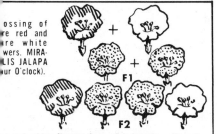

ossing of
re red and
re white
wers. MIRA-
LIS JALAPA
ur O'clock).

F1

F2

d and white flowers form pink hybrids, with red
d white again appearing in F2 generation in this
oportion: 25% pure red, 25% pure white, 50%
nk hybrid.

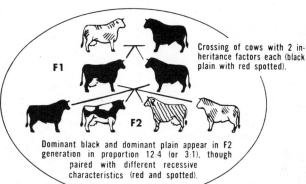

F1

F2

Crossing of cows with 2 in-heritance factors each (black plain with red spotted).

Dominant black and dominant plain appear in F2 generation in proportion 12:4 (or 3:1), though paired with different recessive characteristics (red and spotted).

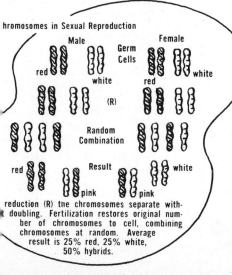

hromosomes in Sexual Reproduction

Male | Female
Germ Cells

red — white
white | red — white

(R)

Random Combination

red — white
Result

pink | pink

reduction (R) the chromosomes separate with-
doubling. Fertilization restores original number of chromosomes to cell, combining
chromosomes at random. Average
result is 25% red, 25% white,
50% hybrids.

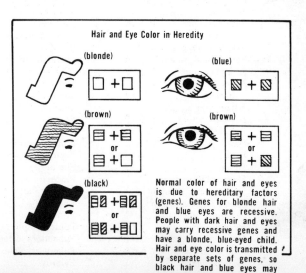

Hair and Eye Color in Heredity

(blonde) — □ + □
(blue) — ▨ + ▨

(brown) — 目 + 目 or 目 + □
(brown) — 目 + 目 or 目 + ▨

(black) — 目目 + 目目 or 目目 + 目□

Normal color of hair and eyes is due to hereditary factors (genes). Genes for blonde hair and blue eyes are recessive. People with dark hair and eyes may carry recessive genes and have a blonde, blue-eyed child. Hair and eye color is transmitted by separate sets of genes, so black hair and blue eyes may appear together.

INDEX